# Acquired for Development By...

## A Hackney Anthology

Influx Press, London

Published by Influx Press
30 Northwold Road, London. N16 7EH
www.influxpress.com

Introduction and selection © Kit Caless and Gary Budden 2012

First published 2012.
2nd Edition published 2012

Printed and bound in the UK by the MPG Books Group,
Bodmin and King's Lynn.

ISBN 978-0-9571693-0-2

# Contents

## IV - Clapton

## V - Hackney Central

## VI - Homerton / Hackney Wick

# Introduction

The idea for this book came to us early in 2011. It is hard to pinpoint what exactly prompted the decision to undertake over a year of hard work and headaches, and making our first forays into the complicated world of publishing.

Perhaps it's best to start by explaining the title of this anthology. Alexander Baron's much lauded sixties Hackney novel, *The Lowlife*, contains the following sentence:

"And as I came away, I saw on a board that epitaph to all our yesterdays, 'Acquired for Development By...'"

It was striking to read something written half a century ago, by a writer from Hackney, that seemed entirely relevant and fitting to the current situation we found ourselves in. Development – or more fittingly for modern times re-development – is something that no resident of Hackney, or all of London for that matter, will be unfamiliar with. It struck us that a pattern was repeating itself, with an official storyline being given to people that was not matching lived experience. The looming Olympics, the luxury flats erupting from Dalston Lane, the facelift of Gillett Square from car-park to culture park – whatever a person's opinion of these things, positive or negative, it struck us that any counter-narrative was being pushed out of the picture. People's memories of things that were physically there, that actually happened, were being bulldozed, tarmacked over, forgotten about.

Not only had physical space been acquired for development, but history, culture and memory also.

We are, of course, aware that there has always been a counter-narrative exploring these themes. However, we feel a point has been reached where a canon has been established, almost presenting an "official" opposing view. We are making a deliberate departure from this, acknowledging these great works of the past, but hoping to move things forward.

What we want to achieve with this anthology is to further this counter-narrative from a new perspective; predominantly that of a younger generation. We are not presenting the truth, merely *a truth*, and are giving voice to a number of personal reflections on place, in Hackney 2011/12, a snapshot of time and place that will become a part of the story that is not, necessarily, officially approved. Before things change again, become re-developed once more, as they inevitably will.

We have divided the book into different areas of the borough. We did this in the hope that readers will draw a sense of the incredible variety of landscapes, both mental and physical, that Hackney provides.

If you walk along the Lea Navigation and wander onto the

marshes opposite, you will find the pylon that Gareth Rees' protagonist in 'A Dream Life of Hackney Marshes' falls for. You might meet some of the houseboat dwellers who Nell Frizzell brings to life in 'Rivers of Change'.

Follow the river down to Hackney Wick and hear echoes of the Hackney Wicked festival evoked so viscerally by Siddartha Bose in 'Wick Love'.

Once you are in the Wick, Colin Priest's concrete visions of 'Dark Island: Wallis Road' will point the way. The ghosts of Rosie Higham-Stainton's 'Paper Corpse' haunt the trail to Homerton, where you'll find the memories of philosophical conversations being exchanged in Eithne Nightingale's 'Foucault Over the Garden Fence'.

Wander down Chatsworth Road and you'll feel the shudders of Kieran Duddy's 'Demolition: Clapton Park Estate 1993' reverberating under the tarmac. At Clapton Pond Ania Ostrowska links a failed relationship and the rise of Tesco in 'Electric Blue'. Cut a left up towards Lower Clapton Road and maybe you'll glimpse the underpants-exposing criminal of David Dawkins' 'A Hackney Triptych'. Head towards Hackney Downs to see where Sam Berkson's 'Hackney Numbers' were added together.

From Amhurst Road you can stride confidently to Hackney Central and try to avoid the dystopian glare of the Orwellian supermarket from Kit Caless' 'Finest Store'. At St. John's Church sit with Isaura Barbé-Brown, listening to her poetic memories of school, family and childhood. You can accept the invitation to a house party in Georgia Myers' 'Sukie's Cherry', or you could follow Andrea Watts from a cashpoint to the Regent's Canal in 'All Gone'.

At the canal, the email transcripts of Lee Rourke's 'http://' will offer you a tantalising peek into a broken relationship. Head up towards Dalston, the epicentre of Hackney's new developments. On the way you can pick over the found history of Paul Case's 'The Battle of Kingsland Road' and immerse yourself in Gary Budden's elliptical 'Tautologies'.

At Dalston, Tim Burrows takes you from the old Four Aces Club to Scotland and back in 'Dalston Kittiwakes'. Jump on Daniel Kramb's bike and cycle down 'Dalston Lane'. Natalie Hardwick finds inspiration in 'Alevism and Hackney'. Gavin James Bower watches 'Tara' working with clients in Shacklewell's backstreets. Brendan Pickett's 'Neo-Noir Hackney Haikus' begin at Ridley Road Market and guide you all the way up to Stoke Newington.

At Stoke Newington you can leap into a totalitarian future with Ashlee Christofferson's '2061', before finally resting, taking a drink and allowing Molly Naylor's 'Pavel's Smokes + Fortune' to let you unwind and contemplate the fragments of life scattered all over our east end neighbourhood.

While this anthology resides in our unique corner of the capital, we hope this collection of work speaks to people outside the borough and captures genuine aspects of modern London life.

Gary Budden & Kit Caless, Hackney, 2012

And as I came away I saw on a board that
epitaph to all our yesterdays,
'Acquired for Development By...'

- Alexander Baron

# Acquired for Development By...

## A Hackney Anthology

I

Lea Valley / Regent's Canal / Hackney Marshes

# A Dream Life of Hackney Marshes

*By Gareth Rees*

## 1. The Big Bang

There was a time before I fell in love with a pylon on Hackney Marshes.

Back then I lived with my girlfriend Ruth in a converted clothes factory in Dalston. I was doing okay writing radio ads, brochures and guide books. I was sent cheques. I laughed on a wobbly bicycle all the way to the bank. We drank the profits and partied all weekend.

One summer day I got married to Ruth in a black lame suit and a cowboy hat. She wore a pretty dress. The sun blazed. A psyche rock band played. We got on a plane to Colombia. The party moved to South America. Bingo bango bosh. Life was still okay.

Then we came back and everything changed.

We bought our own place, the way grownups do. A small flat in Clapton. On the day after we moved in, Ruth discovered she was pregnant. She gave up the drink and I cut down. There were no more parties. I started to watch Saturday night television. For the first time in my life I bought a lawnmower. I listened to Radio 4. There was an apple tree in our garden. How strange, I thought, to own a source of fruit.

When I stepped off the hedonistic treadmill, everything began to ache. My back, my knee, my wrists, my bones. Pain flashed through my fingers when I typed. Sure signs of repetitive strain injury. I spent hours in quiet despair, eating cheese and thinking about death. I grew a big fat Buddha belly.

A physiotherapist told me to spend less time at the computer, lose weight and do more exercise. I ignored her. Another physiotherapist told me the same.

'Just cure my pain.' I requested.


I tried acupuncture. I tried Pilates. I went for a swim at the London Fields Lido. I did everything the experts told me. Nothing helped.

As a last resort I bought a dog. I'd always wanted one, but worried about being tied down. Now I was tied down alright. Strapped to the earth by legions of shrieking responsibilities. The foetus was growing. My wife was vomiting. There was a living room to be painted and furniture to buy. House prices had crashed. And however painful my repetitive strain injury was, the mortgage needed to be paid. To pay it I needed to write more words. And to write, I needed a cure for my pain.

A dog would give me enforced breaks from writing and a dose of exercise. If things got too much with the baby, I had an excuse to flee the house.

Besides, what harm could a dog do?

## 2. Dog

Max came from a breeder in Essex. He was the last in the litter. By the time we got him home I realised I'd never seen his eyes open. I bought a book called *Cocker Spaniels*. Inside was a picture of a 9 week old puppy with bright eyes, glossy coat and long limbs.

I stared at the photo. I stared at Max. He looked like a drowned mole. Fluid oozed from his tear ducts. He had bandy legs and dandruff. He tumbled around the kitchen, leaking piss and bumping into his crate.

'Shall we take him back?' I asked Ruth.

'He's a living thing.' She caressed her bump. 'You can't just send him back.'

The vet told me Max had congenital cataracts. He prescribed steroid drops. The drug kept Max's pupils frozen wide so light could flow round his cataracts and feed his retinas with images.

As soon as he was vaccinated I took him to Millfields park. That was the point after all. Me. The dog. Being out and about.

We made it to the bottom of the slope, where the park plunged into the Lea Navigation. Across the water a concrete peninsula littered with piles of rubble. Seagulls. Barbed wire. Ducks.

On either side of this peninsula were two park exits. A footbridge over the canal and a steel rampart beneath the Lea Bridge Road. Flowing through these vents was a stream of human traffic. Cyclists, runners, dog-walkers, wasters, jabbering loons, couples, spliff-toting teenagers, baseball-capped men on bikes yelling through megaphones at rowing boats.

I'd no idea where they were coming from. I'd never heard of

the Lea Valley nature reserve. All I knew about Hackney marshes was that people played football there on Sundays.

Now I was curious.

As soon as Max was able to walk the distance, I crossed the Rubicon. I took a brief glance behind me at the neat Victorian terraces of Clapton where my wife and unborn baby dwelled. For a moment I considered turning back. Then I passed beneath Lea Bridge Road, where a splash of graffiti read:

YOUR SAFETY, OUR THREAT

## 3. Pylon

Almost immediately I realised this was not London anymore.

Max and I were on a towpath. Narrow-boats lined the navigation, bedecked with pot plants and armchairs. Smoke puffed from their tiny chimneys. A man sawed through a stack of wood. Geese bobbed on the water among Coke bottles and foam.

Set in a long redbrick wall were some iron gates. I entered and found myself on the ruins of a Victorian water filtration plant. Concrete pathways rose from circular beds. Service ladders disappeared into pools of rushes. Fragments of machinery jutted from the ramparts. I ran my hands over defunct cogs and the skeletons of pulley systems. In the centre of it all, a stone circle like a sundial where I spun slowly, amazed.

In one of the filter beds giant ceramic fish heads and tails rose from the rushes. A weir rammed with nappies, cans and footballs gushed water into a river. Cormorants perched on rocks, preening themselves like creatures freshly dragged from an oil slick. A parakeet darted from a tree. Max sniffed at the remains of a sandwich. The air smelled of rotten leaves and bus fumes.

I wondered how such a place could exist on my doorstep. It didn't even feel like a place, but a space in between. A giant crack in the city where the detritus of London collected.

And then I saw her. Lurching from the scrub like a catwalk model, crackling with power and energy. My head told me it was just another electricity pylon but it was – she was – different. I couldn't take my eyes off her.

That's how it began.

The affair. If that's what you want to call it.

Like most of my relationships it started slowly. Max and I walked by her slender steel body every day. But we didn't really connect. Not properly. It still hurts me to think of it. But it's true.

At first, too many other things caught my roving eye.

The abandoned toy factory, brooding by the navigation, windows smashed, loading hook like a torture instrument in the bay. Walthamstow Marsh where long-horned cattle grazed, framed by the silhouettes of City skyscrapers. The vast green sheet of the playing fields, stapled with goal-posts, scuffed and scarred by a million Sunday League matches.

What was known as 'the marsh' was, I discovered, a string of marshes, building yards, bird sanctuaries, reservoirs, railway lines and underpasses. You could get lost in there. Wander into cul-de-sacs littered with fox shit, beer cans and wild flowers. Spend hours among mysterious concrete obelisks. Read graffiti arguments between cyclists, walkers, gangsters and artists. Listen to rats forage in the nettles. Stare down pipes into the bowels of the city. Hear the gurgle of subterranean rivers.

Each day I pushed further down a corridor of electricity pylons stretching from the edge-lands of the A12, along the Eurostar lines, to Springfield Marina and the grand Victoriana of Stamford Hill.

I found the pylons magnificent but predictable. Each one led to the next in an endless parade. These giants were wedded to each other with loops of glass and cable. Manacled like slaves. Forced into enclaves of inaccessible scrub. Outcasts in a world that wished they weren't there, spoiling the view.

She was the exception. Indignant and inconvenient, she stood right there in the Middlesex filter beds, overlooking the art installations, tourist information boards and artificial ponds.

My pylon.

She'd been here all the time, waiting for me to notice her properly.

Funny how that happens in life. In love.

## 4. Birth

From the first day Sophia was born she puked. She shat. She screamed with colic. It was the end of sleep for Ruth and I. The end of sex, the end of meaningful conversation, and – for me – the end of writing.

For the first month I dutifully followed the pair around, bunching nappies into balls, emptying bins. Did what Dads were supposed to do. I hung about in doorways like a demented waiter with a muslin cloth draped over my arm.

'What does she want now?' I said, annoyed that I had to raise my voice over the caterwauling.

'She's hungry,' Ruth said.

'Sorry?'

'SHE IS HUNGRY.'

'What do you want me to do?'

'Nothing, as usual.' Ruth unbuttoned the breast-flaps of her maternity dress.


Christ. There was absolutely nothing good about this.

My wife was confined to the bedroom once again. She spent the days and nights in front of rolling property programmes, feeding like a sow, trying to keep the baby happy. She was fraught with worry. The relentless screaming, it was unnatural. Sophia clung to her with translucent fingers. If I tried to hold her she'd writhe in my arms until I spilled her back onto Ruth's chest.

I bought a glossy hardback book called *Baby* by Desmond Morris. Inside were pictures of pink and peaceful newborn babies.

I stared at the photos. I stared at Sophia. She looked like a stricken bat. Her excrement smelled of sulphur. Ruth would point at the oily green spatter and say, 'Does that look normal to you?'

I had no idea. It wasn't in the Desmond Morris book. I sat in grim silence next to the bed, handing out wetwipes, thinking of my next excuse to leave the room.

If I could manage an escape, I'd catch a little sleep on a rug beneath my desk. Max was usually there, curled up, oblivious. I seethed with envy for the dog's life. It was the only emotion I felt, in truth, but I didn't tell Ruth.

The pylon, though, she'd understand. That much I knew.

I thought my return to work would solve my problems. But the noise was more excruciating than the shooting pains in my arms. Sometimes I'd hear Ruth crying too. I'd turn up the music in my office but it didn't mask the knowledge that they were next door, imploding.

At times I sensed Ruth standing in the doorway of my office behind me, holding our sick, yellow baby. I daren't turn round. Instead I'd hammer gibberish into my computer, as if rapt with inspiration, until she went away. Then I'd kill the words with the delete button.

A health screening company had commissioned me to write a mail order brochure for them. They wanted old people to get checked for their stroke and heart attack risk.

After two weeks I came up with a single headline:

IS YOUR LIFE OVER?

I spent many hours changing the font and text size. Large, small. Ariel. Helvetica. Garamond. Dingbats. Green, then red, then black, highlighted, underlined, in bold.

Then I deleted it and wrote:

READ THIS OR DIE

I blamed the tiredness. But I knew that it wasn't that. Not entirely.

That pylon, she was constantly at the back of my mind. A needle probing at the skin of every thought.

## 5. Vision

In rare moments when the house was quiet I lay face down and sucked air through the gaps in the floorboards. I imagined the micro-world an inch beneath. The lice, the mites, locked in a battle for survival, hunting for food, living a wild life. I imagined that I was her, my pylon, looking down on wretched mankind with benevolence and love. I imagined that she saw me staring back at her, and that she felt a deep longing.

To take my mind off things I watched a lot of television. Programmes about fat people. About unhappy people. About people winning and losing competitions. About people cooking. About people having babies. Always the babies.

The doctor refused to accept there was anything wrong with ours. 'They do cry you know,' he said, giving a great big African belly laugh.

Ruth went crazy at him, demanding to see a specialist. Nurses led her into a backroom and tried to talk her down, stop her weeping. Later I got a phone call from a counsellor enquiring about her postnatal depression.

'Fuck you,' I said, which didn't help. Now we were on a register.

After that I found it was best not to talk at all. Not around Ruth, or nurses, or doctors. So I started to avoid the family altogether. Half-hour dog walks became hour-long walks. Two-hour walks. Sometimes I'd be gone a whole afternoon.

I felt more at home on the marsh, roaming among the London tribes. Tracksuit gangsters with bullmastiffs. Hasidic Jews in high black socks and shiny shoes. Bearded old men with yappy dogs. Vociferous Turks. Pram-pushing Poles with '80s haircuts. Anorak nerds, supping from flasks. Lovers in the long grass. Cyclists with their Lycra bulges. Rastas, hippies, hoodies, transvestites, City boys, construction workers, drunks.

It was like strolling through a collective dream. And it felt good, being outside myself.

But not good enough.

This is why, I think, I started taking my dog's cataract medicine.

The first occasion was a mistake. I rubbed my eyes shortly after administering the drops to Max. Forty minutes later I could feel my irises tear open. Light flooded my retina. The room was submerged in a psychedelic haze, pierced by shards of silver. Like a vision.

For a few hours it was too much. I had to crouch in the wardrobe. Even then, rays of light still penetrated somehow. When I held my hand to my face I realised I could see in the dark. My hand was glowing. It was pylon-shaped.

Ruth mistook my reasons for being in the wardrobe. She stood there with the crying baby, speaking through the door.

'Charlie, I know you're finding this hard. But I don't have the energy to worry about you. I can't deal with two babies.'

'I can't hear you' I said.

'I said that I'm not sorry for you.'

'Sorry?'

'I - AM - NOT - FEELING - SORRY - FOR – YOU.'

I'd had enough. I knew where I had to be right now and it wasn't with Ruth. I stepped out of the wardrobe.

'Max needs a walk.'

Sporting a pair of sunglasses I hurried Max to the bottom of Millfields Park. We turned right under the bridge, as usual, past the weir and over the footbridge, towards the Middlesex filter beds.

Even with shades on there was so much light hitting the back of my eyeballs the world was in whiteout. It felt like I was stumbling towards the pearly gates, towards God. I entered the filter beds and wobbled across the ramparts, pools of fire on either side of me.

I was so desperate to see her I almost broke into a run. But there was no need. She emerged from the dazzle, a slender giant, looking almost wet in the shimmering light, like Ursula Andress striding from the ocean. She cackled and crackled. Lines of black cord whipped from her arms to embrace me.

I went to her, heart pumping. Stood dead centre between her four legs and gazed up. I gasped at the interplay of lines. The poetry of infinity in her delicate spirals of steel. She fired sunbeams at me through her gaping geometry. I laughed in response. I marvelled at the essence of her, trembling with electricity. I touched her legs, each clad in a garter of barbed wire, thrilled at the thought of the volts running through her.

For a moment I imagined her in a black leather miniskirt and I felt an enormous, surprising erection.

But I did nothing about it.

I didn't want to sully the moment.

## 6. Love

Her name was Angel.

You can laugh. You can mock. But go and tell the captain of a ship he's deluded when he calls her by name. Tell that to the mountaineer who loves, fears and respects the peak that could kill him.

To me she wasn't a thing that had been constructed. She was a being who had descended from above. We'd found each other and nothing else mattered. I stopped going to the marina. I grew bored of watching the wrecking balls dismantle the toy factory. Max no longer got to wade in the Lee River's mud-banks or gambol among the upturned shopping trolleys.

Now it was all about Angel. I planned my days around her.

In the morning, I'd help at home with the nappies, the bottles, the puke. All that stuff. Really threw myself into it with gusto, so Ruth wouldn't know something was up. Then I'd go to the kitchen and prepare sandwiches. Triangle ones.

Ruth found me in the kitchen once, carefully measuring the angle of the bread.

'You're making sandwiches.'

I took the cheese out of the wrapper.

'Blue cheese,' Ruth said. 'You hate blue cheese. You say it tastes of metal.'

I froze. Did she suspect something?

'Things change.'

'Whatever, Charlie.'

She shuffled back to her bedroom, closed the door.

I tessellated the triangles in a Tupperware box. Carefully placed the box inside a leather satchel. Then off to the marsh.

That summer a gang of hedonistic narrowboat folk had moored outside the filter bed entrance. They wore trilbies and leather jackets. They cracked open beers in the late morning and wiled away the hours on sofas smoking weed. They blared dubstep from an old ghetto blaster. They laughed a lot.

I'd pass them every day. They'd nod. I'd smile back. It was a happy time. They brought a carnival feel to the place. Every day a celebration. Magical.

Sometimes I'd sit on the bench next to Angel and feel her hum, my legs jiggling in front of me. Max would chase his shadow, or sleep in the shade. When he was settled I'd dab cataract medicine into each eye, wait for my pupils to crank open, the irises to fire up, then out with the iPod.

I'd started recording a series of electronic mixtapes. Drone. Minimalist techno. Really it wasn't my taste. It was hers. I was only interpreting the vibrations. Giving her what she wanted. She loved the glitch sound. Our favourite track was 'Test Pattern #1111' by Ryoji Ikeda, a Japanese sound artist.

Together we'd sing it: 'Chk chk chk chck chck – tsssssssssssssssssssssst – tk tkt tk tk tkt kk – tsssssssssssssssssssss – tk tk tkt tk.'

Afterwards I'd go between her legs and point my camera upwards, let the sun fragment in her girders, spatter rays across my lens. Gently she'd tickle the nape of my neck with volts. It was wonderful.

'Chk chk chk - tsssssssssssssssssssssssst.' I would coo.

'Tk tk tk tk.'

A quick cigarette and I was off round the filter beds, taking pictures from every angle, let her slip in and out of view, play peek-a-boo behind the bushes.

Over the weeks my photo library built up nicely. I kept pictures of her on a secret file named 'Work'. In the first four months of her life we'd taken almost no photographs of Sophia. Why would we? We'd barely left the house as a family. She was constantly in pain.

As for Ruth and I, the happy couple, there was nothing to photograph. We'd vanished from our own marriage. We slept in alternative shifts, passed by each other with a grunt.

In this respect, the cataract medicine was an inconvenient habit. The effects lasted up to twelve hours and made sleep difficult. My head ached all the time. Whisky helped a little. I made sure I always carried a hipflask.

Angel didn't approve of the drinking. The silent treatment; always a giveaway. But I reasoned that relationships were all about accepting the idiosyncrasies of others. Drinking was mine, being an electricity pylon was hers.

But they were good days, mostly. At dusk I'd return, happy, from the marsh to find my family slumped like refugees in front of a flickering television. Often Ruth would murmur something at me, 'I miss you,' or 'I love you'. I couldn't make it out. Never replied. My head was always banging with pain. I'd slide straight under the duvet.

Then one night Ruth wasn't in bed. She was sitting in the living room with a brown envelope, trembling.

'I opened this,' she said. 'It's from the bank.'

'Right.' The letter didn't surprise me. I'd not done a single day's useful work in almost five months. The money had entirely run out. Letters were piling up. Bills. Overdrawn warnings. Council tax. Threats. I'd taken to stuffing them behind the filing cabinet so Ruth wouldn't see.

'But all that work you're doing on the computer...'

Electronic music mixtapes, arranging photos. These took time. Especially when your eyes were fucked. She'd never understand.

'It's all in hand,' I promised.

'Charlie.' Ruth had a tone in her voice I'd not heard before. Genuine fear. And I could tell it wasn't about the money.

'Really, it's fine.'

It wasn't though. It wasn't fine. That following morning I took Max on the usual route. Through Millfields. Down to the navigation. On my back was a rucksack full of unopened mail. I decided my only recourse was to bury it somewhere near Angel. I looked up to her. She'd been around longer than I had. She provided the city with energy, with life, for God's sake. Surely she'd know what to do about a trivial matter like this.

As I reached the entrance, I was surprised to see one of my narrowboat friends up and about, a rollie glued to her bottom lip. It wasn't even 9am. She clutched what looked like a plastic cup of wine.

I was even more surprised when she spoke to me.

'You're the pylon guy, right?'

'Pardon?'

'The pylon guy.'

'I'm not sure I…'

'It's okay,' she said. 'You'd better know. Aaron's back. Says he wants to talk to you.' She gestured towards the filter beds.

'Aaron.'

'Old bloke, hangs around the marsh. You must have seen him. He doesn't stop talking about you anyway.'

'I don't think, I…' I shrugged.

'Her fella' she said.

Snap. Crack.

Max with a twig in his mouth, grinning.

Me with my heart broken.

## 7. Rival

I entered the filter beds, trembling. She was there of course. Looking resplendent against a white sky and – I have to say – relieved to see me.

Beneath her a stooped figure waited with a black Labrador. He must have been sixty or more. Grey hair bristled from beneath a baseball cap. His white t-shirt was far too big for him. Far too young for him.

It was hard to make out his facial features, what with my eyes being the way they were. But I could see what looked like egg stains on his beard, and down his chest. Or maybe it was phlegm. He had a dirty hacking cough.

Look at the state of him, I thought. This Aaron bloke. What the hell is she doing with him?

The dogs circled each other, the Labrador growling.

'He's alright' said Aaron in a mildly cockney accent. 'He's old. Bit blind in one eye. Gets snappy.'

'Max's sight's not good either.'

'Cataracts,' he said.

'How did you know?'

'Got my own eyes.' I couldn't quite tell, but it felt like he was giving me a conspiratorial wink. I seethed.

After a long pause he said 'You've come for her, then?'

'I'm sorry?'

'Her,' he jerked his head at Angel. I could sense her flinch. 'Sorry to say mate but you don't have long.'

'I'm not sure...'

'You shouldn't be here,' he said. 'It's not your place.'

But the marsh wasn't anyone's place, I reasoned silently. How dare he? I considered hitting him.

'She's not supposed to be here either' Aaron said. 'I can see why you two get along. Take a look at that.'

He jabbed his stick towards a laminated A4 sign taped beside the pylon. I stared at the text, but my vision was blurred.

'I don't know what it says.'

'They're trying to prettify the marshes. Clean it up. The fucking Olympics. Another excuse for them to get their mitts on things I reckon.'

'But what does the sign actually say?'

'It's a notice of works,' he said. 'They're coming to take her down.'

## 8. Death

There was a time before I fell in love on Hackney Marshes. When things were okay. I wrote ads. I got paid. I was in love with Ruth. We laughed a lot. But I couldn't dwell on the past. I had to think about the here and now.

I tipped the unanswered bank demands from my rucksack and replaced them with tools. Anything I could find.

A hammer. A knife. A spanner.

Ruth knew there was something wrong. With the baby, I mean. And at last the doctors agreed she was right. Sophia had a serious food intolerance problem. Wheat, lactose, gluten, milk, soy, eggs. Whatever Ruth consumed her breasts would turn into liquid poison.

And there she was thinking everything was my fault.

There was a whole load of medical stuff to read about, apparently, but I couldn't keep my attention on it. Ruth sat me down with the letter from the doctor and told me it was a turning point. Sophia would get better and better from now on.

'Now we can get you the help you need,' she said, rubbing a hand through my hair. My spine tingled. I couldn't remember the last time we touched.

But what help did I need? What the hell could Ruth do about my situation?

They were coming the next morning, contract workers in yellow jackets, with their machinery. And they were going to dismantle Angel, piece by piece. In preparation they'd erected blue hoardings around the base of her legs. I'd been watching them come and go from a bird hide I'd built in the bushes.

The way they acted around her, laughing, joking, it was disgusting.

If she'd been an old oak she'd have dozens of hippy tree-huggers chained to her trunk by now. This pylon had stood watch over these beds for decades. She'd kept the city lit, boiled the people's kettles, provided their shitty television programmes, warmed their babies' bottles.

This was the thanks she got.

I was all she had left. That Aaron, he was a flake. Since the day I ran from him in tears he'd completely vanished. Not a trace. I asked the woman from the narrow boat if she'd seen him.

'Dunno who you're talking about,' she told me, straight-faced.

'The old bloke from the marshes!' I cried. 'Her fella!'

'Sure it was me?'

'Yes, but you were drunk... out of it... maybe you don't remember.'

'Cheeky fuck. You should take a look at yourself, chum.'

Well, what did it matter? Part of me was glad he'd gone. He must have been watching me with her for a long time before he dared to confront us. Once he'd seen how serious we were he'd turned tail and fled. The coward.

Not me. I had a plan.

When darkness came I put good use to the cataract drops. I could see very clearly as I approached the locked gate of the filter beds and made my ascent. As I dropped, a fox scuttled into the bushes and poked his nose out, thinking I couldn't see him. The fool. I hissed at him. Moved on with my mission.

The hoardings were a trickier climb. It took a few run-ups, but once I had my fingertips over the rim I could pull myself up, using the hinges of the hoarding as a foot grip.

Once on the other side I settled beside Angel and unpacked my whisky and my tools. I touched her leg. She shivered as if cold.

But I knew it wasn't the cold.

'Don't worry,' I reassured her. 'Tk tk tk tk tk tk tsssssssssssssst.'

I wasn't afraid. These jobsworths would hardly risk their safety to tackle an armed man first thing in the morning. They'd have to phone the boss. Call the police. Get the local press down here.

A right big hoo-ha. That's what I expected.

I tried to stay awake but the whisky overpowered me. It was only an engine and the chatter of workmen that alerted me the next morning. I scrabbled to my feet and peered through a slit in the hoarding.

There were four of them climbing out, and beyond, a white van approaching. Almost certainly there would be more of them inside.

A hot sun beat down. My heart was tight. I clenched the spanner. I breathed deeply and slowly.

I waited.

# Fibre Optic Tree

*By Anita DeMahy*

Dad's ninth storey apartment rests in a Hackney project complex among the stars

One single compartmentalized unit of drugged and drunken bachelorhood

Christmas glowers at curious knick knacks glistening buoyantly from corners of the flat, as if showing homage to the fibreoptic tree standing in the center of the studio space

I look around my 'room'

Which has been outlined by a sheet, slung over one of those car wire harness things, then slung from the pipes that line the ceilings

He tried

A menacing display of Santa Claus and his reindeer, borrowed from my nan's house, blinks loudly beneath the letters

'M RRY CHRISTM S'

# Rivers of Change

*By Nell Frizzell*

*Hidden away on the backwaters of the River Lea is a Hackney community for whom running water, flushing toilets, working fridges and adequate heating is little more than a pipe dream. Which is just the way they like it. But, with British Waterways tightening up the rules on river boat living in London, is the constant cruising canal boat community of Hackney under threat? Or will these arteries of countryside continue to flow unchecked?*

Believe me, my young friends, there is nothing, absolutely nothing, half so much worth doing as simply messing about in boats.

I should know. Like rats, gulls and the odd floating condom, I've been hanging around boats ever since I was a twinkle in my father's eye. Or a bulge in his briefs, anyway. From the custom-made barge my mother sold to go to India (only to return married, blonde and pregnant with my sister), to the Oxford University boats my dad built after being made redundant, to the punts on which I broke my teenage heart, to the steady stream of canal barges that chug past my Clapton window, I've lived a life pitted and puckered by boats.

While boats in Oxford have a certain twee, *Wind in the Willows* familiarity, a Hackney boat is a different kettle of kippers all together. Who, other than a Hackney boater, lives ten minutes from the tube, but has to spend hours every week chopping wood with a hand axe? Who, other than a Hackney boater overlooks the Olympics, but is awoken at 4am every morning by the sound of jaggering coots? Who, other than a Hackney boater, can see the Gherkin from their roof, but has to empty a chemical toilet? Who, other than a Hackney boater, owns an Oyster card but can turn their house around to catch the evening sun?

Of course, like most joggers, walkers, weekenders and music video directors, I used to think of these boats as little more than suburban decoration. A smattering of semi-submerged vessels to walk past on my way to a café or a park. Two boats changed all this.

The first was the Maid Marian. A boat so preposterously small that I could probably hide it under my duvet cover. From bow to stern the whole thing isn't much more than ten feet long and yet it is painted, polished and pampered like a stately home. The idea that someone in Hackney was living in a space even smaller than my own one-bedroom flat wasn't just comforting; it laughed in the face of physics. The second was a beautiful pea green boat, which looked more like an ocean-going frog hiding from naval command than something you'd find floating up the River Lea. I was desperate to know who was living in there, where they hung their washing, how they stored their food, if they missed television, what they did if they ran out of tampons at 2am, where they kept their socks, if they could hang pictures on their walls and a hundred other tiny, almost meaningless details.

The final thing that persuaded me that E5 river life was a world worth watching was the day I saw Italian boater and ex-squatter Catarina drag at least eight litres of water over an icy bridge and back to her floating home, on a bitter February morning. That a modern woman was living with all the comfort of my sour-faced, sheep-farming Welsh grandparents and actually seemed to be enjoying it, blew my mind.

So, I decided to set about interviewing this strange floating community. I would swallow my pride, my reserve and my land-lubbing unfriendliness and just ask these people how they made toast, why their boat was named after a tortured Danish prince, whether they were scared of rats, if they also worked from Monday to Friday and, most importantly of all, what the hell you do with a chemical toilet.

It took a few months to actually get around to meeting Catarina, and even longer to get invited in to her borrowed, wood-lined barge. But once we sat down at her window-lit table, the conversation flowed like ginger beer at a *Famous Five* reunion. This was partly due to the fact that Catarina was drinking coffee so strong it made my eyebrows curl (constantly topping her cup up with sugar, as my Dictaphone vibrated across the table) and partly because Catarina is incensed at the new measures being enforced by British Waterways. 'It's going to be a disaster for everybody,' she thundered at top speed. 'It's completely insane. 'They want everyone to move once a week, at least eight miles in one direction. You know, people live here and work here. Some people have kids. There's going to be so much traffic on the river, it will be chaos. There will be pollution from all the boats moving about and that's not good for the animals. And what about the rowers? And the kayakists. There will be no space for them.'

The subject of British Waterways reform is one that came up during every single conversation I had with the Hackney boaters. Yet it is one that appears to have, so far at least, slipped under the radar of public attention. It is a complicated issue – coloured by rumour, exaggeration and spin – but as far as I can tell British Waterways have proposed to divide the River Lea into six separate neighbourhoods, from Limehouse in the South to the end of the Stort Navigation in the North. All boaters with a constant cruising license – as opposed to a permanent, rented mooring - must travel in one single direction, through those neighbourhoods, moving at least every fourteen days. If they do not move after fourteen days, they will be fined £20 a day if they pay in advance, or £40 a day if they pay after the event. Finally, constant cruising boaters must not stay in one single neighbourhood for more than sixty-one days a year and cannot return to a neighbourhood unless they have 'reached a terminus' i.e. been all the way to Limehouse or Hertfordshire respectively.

The boaters suggest several reasons for the proposals, from 'clearing up' the river in preparation for the Olympics, to earning British Waterways more money now that they've lost their quango funding. British Waterways argue that the rules aren't actually changing, simply being more rigorously enforced, in response to the forty per cent rise in the number of boats along the River Lea in the last five years.

Of all of the responses, a man called John who lives on the river because it is the cheapest way he can be near his daughter's school, has my favourite. 'They can tell me that they're fining me £20 a day but it doesn't necessarily mean that I've got to get a £20 note out of my pocket and give it to them,' John argued, as we sat on the back of his tiny, entirely solar-powered boat. 'It just means I've got to walk around for the rest of my life owing them £20. Or £200.

Or £200,000. Or whatever number they say. It's still just a number. People who haven't got money can't be made to pay for things. A boat that won't move, won't move. A person that can't afford to pay, won't pay. It doesn't really matter how many people sit in meetings and write things on pieces of paper, you can't actually change those things. It's a law of nature.'

If this sounds like so-much philosophical denial in the face of financial punishment, consider for a moment just how much John's response differs from, say, the government's attitude to national debt and borrowing. The money simply isn't there. If it isn't there, it can't be taken. If it can't be taken, it doesn't matter how much you owe. It is just a number.

Which is not to say that all boaters have no money; they just don't have very much money. Catarina works as a cook and a gardener, John sells books in Hampstead along with his friend Paddy, Rosie sells jewellery, Lorraine from The Sandwich Barge does exactly what she says on the tin, while others carry out odd jobs for fellow boaters, write books and play in bands. In short, these are the people who, twenty years ago, would have moved to Hackney because it was a cheap place to be creative. 'A lot of the people on the boats now were in the squats ten or fifteen years ago,' says John. 'I came to Hackney twenty-six years ago from Bingley in Yorkshire and there were whole housing estates squatted, pubs squatted, Jamaican and African music pubs of various levels of legitimacy. It was a very exciting, bohemian place to come to after a Yorkshire Dales village. But now Hackney's sort of grown up with me. I've got an eight-year-old daughter and Stoke Newington is all about young parents with three-wheeled buggies. It's all very strange; I came when I was twenty and it was a party town. Now I'm in my forties and it's a middle aged town.'

Paddy, a self confessed 'crap Buddhist', aims to set up a book barge with John. They want to sell second-hand books to the tourists, walkers and weekenders attracted to the River Lea, in part, by the very boats British Waterways are concerned about. He also came to river life relatively late.

'My grandmother died and left me a bit of money,' Paddy explains, as his cats patter about the boat, eventually curling up by my knee in a patch of early summer sun. 'I thought, "Oh no, this means I'm going to have to get a mortgage now." And I got a terrible cold feeling every time I thought about that. But I knew someone who was living on the river and I used to come running down here on the rare occasions that I tried to give up smoking.

Here, exactly here, was where I imagined living. I bought the boat from a nice old Buddhist drummer who had bought it as a shell and spent four years lovingly putting all the woodwork in. He sold it to buy a seventy-foot boat, in which he could put his drum kit.'

Eddie, a man who also plans to trade his barge in for a larger model so he can house his collection of instruments, came to river living after a similar Road to Damascus moment. 'I lived on a boat in my twenties. Then I got married and she didn't want to. I was so much in love and so much being a father, I didn't realise that I would be left with a despot like I was,' Eddie tells me, as we sit on plastic chairs by the river drinking strong tea and playing with his three dogs. 'I was having a real mid-life crisis when a friend took me to his boat in Cambridge. He had this little boat here and I bought it off him, over three years ago.'

'I used to be in loads of bands,' Eddie continues. 'Mainly guitar and mouth organ, although I don't mind playing the keyboard. It was more fun than a career, although I was asked quite a few times. Me and musicians don't really get on; I don't have the same ego as them. I don't think I'm all powerful, great and marvellous.'

Since buying his boat Eddie hasn't only re-plumbed and re-wired it, he has also decorated it with eight colourful Perspex circles, making it one of the most conspicuous boats on the river. Imagine Timmy Mallet, made maritime. 'I got them from an old job I did years ago,' he explains. 'It was primarily to stop the kids using the boat as target practice. But it looked so funky and it's so lovely when the light comes through in the morning that I just left them on. She's a bit on the shabby side, but it brightens her up a little. She's called Rocker because she's got a convex bottom; she literally rocks.'

Talking of names, the River Lea is awash with the sort of puns usually reserved for hairdressers, word play usually associated with broadsheet crosswords and monikers that say possibly more about the owner than they're willing to admit. There's the *Onion Bargee, Sans Souci, The Hobbit, Roadrunner, Quest* and, a personal favourite, *Tuppence*. So, is this evidence that Hackney is a hub of red-top sub-editors? Apparently not. 'Normally you don't change the name of your boat when it's in the water because it's meant to be a bad omen,' explains Lorraine, the owner of The Sandwich Barge. Well, the business is called The Sandwich Barge – the boat is actually called *Greenfinch* after the original owner, Mr Finch. The only way to re-name a boat is to take it out of the water, smash a bottle of champagne against it and generally act like aristocratic pagans, as far as I can tell.

'We debated changing the name when she was out of the water,' the owners of *Hamlet* tell me. 'But the guy who owned this before and named it Hamlet had died, so it seemed a bit wrong to change it again. Eventually we kind of grew to love it. It's a masculine name and most boats are considered females.'

Hamlet looks, it must be said, more like a floating 1970s cigar box than a canal boat, making her probably my favourite bit of graphic design on the whole of the River Lea. Not that I could persuade her owners: 'We're going to strip her right back and paint her black with a cream top,' they told me, my face falling like a cake off a plate.

Luckily, other boaters are more willing to embrace the quirky aesthetic of river living. 'Me and my boyfriend are both creatives,' Rosie tells me, as she eats lunch and reads the paper on the roof of her boat, which is called *Ionic*. 'I make jewellery and he makes hats and cycling apparel. I have client meetings here, which I think is more romantic. It's an experience.'

Of course, finding bike-orientated creatives in Hackney is about as difficult as finding hairs on a Labrador, but does living on a boat really suit the artistic entrepreneur? 'I don't want to say it's a cheaper way of life,' says Rosie, 'but you don't have all the bills and you're not tied down. It is a harder way of life though, too. I'd say we move every three weeks, but if they're going to make it every two weeks then I think it would become too difficult for me. I'm trying to start a small business, so I need to be close to my studio.'

This sense of dissatisfaction and disappointment seems far more common among the Hackney boaters than Catarina's caffeine-fuelled fury. 'British Waterways are the only downside I've experienced in my boating life,' Paddy tells me, between Golden Virginia roll-ups and sips of coffee. 'All they seemed to do for the last two years is spend money on making sure people have boat licenses and safety certificates. Now they've lost their money, which means the Great British thing will happen, which is that slowly but slowly, someone begins to regulate every element of your life.'

Regulation and river life seem, if not completely at odds, then certainly distant cousins. Hackney boaters, as far as I have learned from my marsh-side conversations, are independent, practical and relaxed people who seem relatively unfazed by the odd bit of uncertainty.

'We've always been quite nomadic' Pat, the owner of *The Lord Nelson* tells me, from the snug living quarters of the seventeen foot boat he shares with his wife. 'When we were younger I used to ring up in the summer and say "Fancy a run out? Come and pick me up." We had a trailer and a tent. We'd put the trailer on the car, the dog in the back and off we'd go. Just pick a spot on the map and spend the weekend there. Or when the kids were very young we used to just take a bag of sandwiches, a bottle of orange and walk the canals, all the way from Hammersmith. We've always loved the open air.' Pat and his wife Mavis used to run holidays for disabled people, many of which took place on barges. So it is perhaps unsurprising that, once they had retired, they moved onto an ex-hire barge. 'It's great for arguments,' Pat tells me, chuckling. 'She'll go out the front with her book and I'll go out the back with my fishing rod. You do need a bit of space between you but, I mean, seventeen foot is quite a lot of space.'

I had imagined, when I first started interviewing the River Lea boaters that constant cruisers like Mavis and Pat would be slightly out of kilter with their young, Hackneyite neighbours. But the sense of community along the river appears stronger than I credited. 'One thing I would like to say is that the people along the canals are absolutely brilliant people,' Pat told me. 'No matter how rough they look. If you need or want something they'll help you. You've just got to ask.'

This sense of community, of friendliness, was echoed by every single boater I spoke to. 'I've never lived in London so happily,' said Paddy, who lived and worked in the capital as a drugs counsellor for over fifteen years. 'These are arteries of countryside, running through the city. Country rules apply socially. We're sitting here talking to each other now because you wondered past and said "hello". That's normal social engagement on a boat. I know all my neighbours. I watch out for their boats and they watch out for mine. This is the first time that I've known my neighbours in London.'

At the risk of going all Tiny Tim on this, Hackney land residents would be hard-pushed to equal the kind of kinship shown by Hackney boaters. For instance, Lorraine, with an attitude to sanding and grouting that makes me want to drink cement out of a work boot, described how it was her boating friends who helped bring The Sandwich Barge into existence: 'I did it all from recycled material – I went to skips, I went to building sites. I didn't have any money, so I asked people. Once they heard what I was doing they were all very, very helpful. I made big roast dinners and fat breakfasts and a few beers here and there. I love the feel, the community and the people around here. People look at you in a different light.'

So, if there is community, freedom, cheaper living, an artery of countryside, tranquillity and solar power, what single thing do the boat residents of Hackney still think would radically improve their lives? The answers are as disparate and idiosyncratic as the people who give them. Rosie asks for 'a supermarket boat selling fresh fruit, or an allotment boat that we all work on. Or maybe a hairdryer.' For book man Paddy it would have to be 'A twice-a-day corner shop boat. It would sell you fags and biscuit treats that you want immediately, rather than walking twenty mins to the shop'. The owners of *Hamlet* would 'Love a solar powered fridge', while Eddie believes that all his wishes have already come true with the Chinese mass production of cheap, efficient LEDs. Lorraine would 'Like the engine to run on water,' and Catarina is dreaming of 'A little outdoor shower and a surf board.'

'The best thing about boat life,' Lorraine told me, 'is that no-one can really touch you. You're out in the middle of the water.' With that, it seemed, she encapsulated the very essence of River Lea life and just why the actions of British Waterways are feared and fought as strongly as they are.

'We acknowledge that our past relaxed control of moorings on the Lea area waterways has been responsible for the emergence of what we now see as a problem,' British Waterways recently stated on their website. 'There may be different views on the extent to which there is currently an imperative to curb growth in the number of boats on the river without home moorings, but there can be little doubt that continued growth will lead to reduction in amenity for both land and water-based communities. A practical plan for moorings is therefore essential.'

Of course, a practical plan is essential. But what cannot be underestimated is the extent to which the boat owners along the River Lea see this patch of Hackney as their home. Leo Hickman may have called the River Lea 'one of the country's most polluted rivers', but I very much doubt that the footballs, prams, plastic bags of dog shit, bottles, chicken boxes and fag butts that float down the river are dropped there by boaters. It is us, the landlubbers, who cause that particular problem. In fact, it is the boaters who keep the banks of the Lea clear and, most importantly for me, safe. 'One of the things that we're proposing to British Waterways,' Rosie tells me, 'is that we pay a bit less but everyone works together to do litter collecting and work as a community to look after the river.'

As a runner, I am far more comfortable jogging past this

familiar group of floating homes and homeowners, than I would be a transient collection of cruising boats or, worse still, an empty tow path. Like British Waterways I don't want the river to become congested by boats; as a lifelong green obsessive I hate the idea that this microcosm of countryside may become over-run by people. But I also don't want to have a whole, long-standing community of Hackney residents pushed out of their neighbourhood by impractical or unworkable proposals. Especially as they seem so happy here.

'Out of all the living that I've done,' says Eddie, who has travelled the road, run restaurants, driven dog-drawn carriages through London and lived on campsites, 'living on the water is the nicest.'

Perhaps, as Hackney residents, that little bit of niceness is all we need.

# http://

*By Lee Rourke*

## 1. The phone call

The phone call was about to draw to a close. A long, drawn-out affair where nothing of much importance was actually relayed; mostly just the ums and ahs of everyday speech, all neatly published within the parameters and confines of developing digitization. Hoodwinked from the very start, it had to draw to a close.

'And that's your reason?'

'Er, yes, that's it.'

'Because it doesn't seem real? Because you don't see enough of me? We are not real? That's your reason?'

'Yes, in a nutshell.'

'Pathetic.'

'No. Merely the truth. As it is.'

'As you see it.'

'As I see it.'

## 2. Two hours later

Two hours later the following message/update was published on facebook:

**_____ _____ is now listed as single.**

## 3. The evening spent

The evening was spent watching TV. Alone, in the bedroom of a fourth floor apartment in Clapton, East London. Only to be interrupted by sporadic toing and froing to the kitchen for food (6 x rounds of toast (made intermittently in rounds of one)) and hot drinks throughout the night (3 x tea, 2 x coffee, 1 x hot chocolate, 1 half-filled bottle of Evian). Sleep was uneasy and several bathroom visits were made. Sleep came eventually, much like a battery running out of life. An email appeared in a hotmail account's inbox early the following morning, the laptop transmitting the missive, hard-drive humming on the pillow beside a weary head:

Phone Call
From: _____ _____ (_____78@hotmail.com)
Sent: 06 May 2009 06:33:50
To: _____ (_____@hotmail.co.uk)

*My love (you horrible/beautiful bastard),*

*I know that phone call was hard. If it's any comfort (not that you want it, I suppose) it was hard for me too. I never thought that it would end this way. I never thought for one moment that you not being here, with me, in the present, would cause such hurt. All I can say is your slipping away from me, your moving towards the unreal, its distance from me, your slide away from our reality has cut me to the bone. Deep down I am bleeding for you. I feel that I am forever running after you; that you are – quite unintentionally, in your own unique way, I admit – leaving me behind, making it impossible for me to keep up. I am forever running after you; waiting for you. I can hang on no more. I know it's not your fault. How can it be your fault? You asked for none of this. I created you (if you think about it). You are you, that's all you can be. But, this moving away from me, towards what I cannot reach, into the unreal, it's all too much for me. I know, I know, I repeat myself endlessly. But, I can't go on with this now. This is my retreat, back to where things were so much simpler for the both of us; back here where I feel safest; it's where our reality lies. If you can understand one thing, then it must be this: I am doing this to save myself. I do not want to slide into the abyss with you. I need to remain here now. My feet firmly on the ground beneath them.*

*Standing in reserve for you,*
  *X*

## 4. A slanting light

A slanting beam of light, cast from the lamp on the desk, becomes visible. The dust motes within it react to the circulation of stale air within the room. You look at the screen. It flickers momentarily, as if some slight electrical surge has suddenly entered the room. But it hasn't, it was just a flicker of something, maybe it wasn't on the screen after all, maybe it appeared inside your own cranium, some superfluous pulse-bleeps of neural activity detonated in a nanosecond, over before you could trace their appearance? As mere *flickers* such as these tend to do.

You're looking at the entrance to Regent's Canal, the steps on the corner of Baring Street and New North Road at the boundary of Hackney and Islington. It's there, before you, elongated upon the 17″ widescreen of your laptop. It's real. More *real* than you could ever imagine. You're looking at the steps through the prism of Google Maps. You stare at the entrance, leading down to the canal below. Gainsborough Studios can be seen on the far bank, its balconies and identikit flats and apartments stare blankly back at you. It's here that you shall wait and _____ _____ will hopefully appear. You've already sent out the coordinates, there was no need to do anything else:

http://maps.google.co.uk/maps?f=q&source=s_q&hl=en&geoco
de=&q=N1&sll=53.800651,-4.064941&sspn=18.98626,52.77832&
ie=UTF8&ll=51.536272,-0.089436&spn=0.018659,0.051541&z=15
&layer=c&cbll=51.536213,-0.089545&panoid=X5nLrciOFBZdLB
jzr1qQGA&cbp=12,158.29139449703004,,0,5

You know that everything is now in place; that everything has already been documented: a place for both of you to exist.

You are thinking:


*Just click on these coordinates, click on them, I will be waiting for you here; it's where I shall wait for you, by the canal, by the entrance, just there, where we can be together. I will wait for you, you'll be able to see me there, or I'll be able to see you there when you arrive, by the entrance, and I shall come to meet you and we can exist here, we can meet here and you'll find me here and we'll be together right here, we'll <u>really</u> be just here for all to see and there we'll be, not here, but there, <u>in the screen,</u> there where I can see where we shall be and you will find me and I will find you, in the screen, mapped, documented, coordinated, un-separated, <u>pixellated,</u> together without the need to be anything other than ourselves or something else . . .*


You click on the coordinates, looking at the shadows cast by the trees. You're sure they just moved, you're sure the shadow is eking across your screen. You wait. Hoping, knowing that _____ _____ will somehow appear, that it will happen and you will go there.

## 5. In this waiting

In this waiting is a reality that you've never felt before. Somehow, as things fly all around you, past you, over you, beneath you, all you have is the urge to get there. Waiting to get there. To be together again.

# II

## Dalston

# Dalston Lane

*By Daniel Kramb*

You raise your head.
You clear your throat:
You go.
Not looking left or right,
you stride,
once again, on a swelling
confidence
(Ha! you say),
determined to ditch…

– in your back, the nu-neon that says
DALSTON JUNCTION
puts Café Bliss into perspective,
its reds and yellows
coming off
opposite scaffolding that's wrapping more
of your shiny tower's same –
…and step by step,

you discard
the crumbling
remains…

– Funeral Directors EST 1881
and the China Man (dead),
behind walls of corrugated iron
in a thick anarcho-black
of ashes, rot & piss; Sound
& Music –

…of a burdensome past,
(Ha! you say),
because you've left your past
behind
a long time ago; you
jump
the red that signals
convention
and rush on…

– between the washed-out white
of biked-up balconies,
the majestic tower of St Mark's
appears, for just a moment,
then disappears,
again, it's brown spires towards
the up-there –

…where a God might,
or might not,
hang out, but you're dropping
that question
(Ha! you say),
for this proud parade
past
The Three Compasses…

– the day-time drinkers don't even
spare you a glimpse
as they bemoan,
their self-rolled cigarettes
in a wrinkled half-hold,
a dying community –

…that out-moded
construct you're dumping,
eyes ahead
(Ha! you say),
having long replaced it
with your own rules,
as you hurry on…

– on your right, Healthy Stuff
smells like a harbinger,
still tightly wrapped
in a heady stream
of a thousand languages,
clashing
in their richness,
this street's most beautiful song –

…which you don't hear,
ears closed,
heading on; you
kick
the vague ghost of a so-called
ideology
(Ha! you say.
What no one needs:)
another shadow
of a shadow
of a belief; you
haste on…

– nothing grabs your attention,
amid the vagaries of other flats,
other people,
until a redbrick Brook Community
Primary
sends a wave
of uniformed screams at you –

…but their voices of innocence
are drowned
by your shedding of
ballast,
ballast,
ballast,
as you gallop on,
once again
ridding yourself
(Ha! you say)
of all that's holding you back…

– on the other side, flat-pack flats
in grey and white
and nothing
rubs the inevitable Express
(7am-11pm),
until there's that railway bridge,
crossing
in a rusty red –

…the final barrier!
that's preventing you,
oh, modern human,
from freeing
yourself;
from leaving behind
everything!
that might hinder your glorious conquest…

– centuried water
drip
drip
drips
onto dusty carpets, half-price,
and Michael's Flowers,
as the pigeons shit
into the semi darkness
that echoes
your getting there –

…before you stumble out,
smiling at yourself,
oh, freest of beings,
for having made it, once again,
into the land
that only knows yourself
U-N-T-I-L
you reach the junction, so wide
and open,
and real, suddenly:

too many streets in far too many directions,
and
you're looking up (Ha?)
and
you're looking on (Ha?)
and
you keep standing there,
as you realise
(Ha?)
that you have no idea where to turn to,
all guidance left to litter Dalston Lane.

# Dalston Kittiwakes

*By Tim Burrows*

SPRING 2011: PHASE ONE OF DALSTON SQUARE HAS BEEN COMPLETED, INCLUDING DUNBAR TOWER, NAMED AFTER NEWTON DUNBAR OF THE FOUR ACES CLUB THAT ONCE EXISTED ON THE SITE.

On Dalston Lane, across the street from the new Barratt blocks, Newton Dunbar pulls a photograph out of an envelope. It depicts a ruin. Not the ruin of the Victorian theatre which held the Four Aces – the club that Newton invested half his life in – was eventually allowed to become before it was demolished, making way for the towers that rose from nothing almost overnight, and now dwarf the surrounding area. But a heap of stones positioned three-hundred- and-seventy-odd miles north in East Lothian, on the east coast of Scottish border country.

The significance lay in the name of the ruin, Dunbar Castle. The picture was taken by a girlfriend of Newton's former associate Charlie Collins during a holiday that the couple had taken during the early 90s. Collins had laid the foundations of the Four Aces in the mid 1960s, booking artists such as Stevie Wonder in this former theatre and cinema, before he was approached by Newton who was looking for a new location to house his Highbury-based soul and ska-heavy club. Collins soon took off to Jamaica, where he recorded out-there rocksteady sessions under the name of 'Sir' Collins. Newton stayed put and ran the Four Aces for thirty three years, reflecting the evolution of Jamaican music from ska to rocksteady to roots to dub to lovers to dancehall to jungle and beyond.

That this club was run by the same Jamaican-born man (Newton had moved to England when he was 18, starting the club almost a decade later) for over three decades is remarkable. Today, London's longest running reggae club has become a symbol of the cultural absences felt in this part of East, going on Northeast London. When Newton finally lost the battle the club had been in the sights of Hackney Council and several developers, for years. He was handed a compulsory purchase order in 1998, and left the building for the last time in 1999, to make way for a cinema that never came. The theatre first opened in 1886. It had held a circus, variety theatre and cinema before part of it became home to the Four Aces. It was demolished in 2007 after much resistance from the community and the anarchists that had been squatting it in an attempt to halt the destruction. Four Barratt Homes tower blocks were erected on the site next to the new Dalston Junction station in 'Phase One' of the Dalston Square project. Provocatively and without Newton's consent, one of them was named Dunbar Tower.

All that exists of the Four Aces today are fragments of evidence. Stories scattered around online message boards, shared by those who'd stayed up all night and sweated. Those who'd got lost with bent minds in the warrens and crannies of the club's ungovernable building. Sketchy accounts from ravers, employees tell stories of bliss and violence at the legendary jungle night, Labrynth, some of which was caught on camera by Winstan Whitter who made the 2008 documentary *Legacy In The Dust*. Archived moments that had burned a mark in time, now boxed-up, historical curiosities. Remembrances of an era when decisions could be taken by people about the forward-motion of their community. Dredged up memories that try to combat consensual amnesia – recollections by those who could mutter, 'I was there,' with an unerring gaze. All eventually become soundbites, conjuring up images that melt in the minds of prospective clients and investors, those wishing to buy into the new logic of an area that is obliged to have a misspent past to define it.

Down the new East London Line, a mile or two south, is the financial sector outfall: bars, open-all-hours strip clubs, golfing ranges and five-a-side pitches surround Shoreditch High Street. Not long ago an artist haven - hence, up-and-coming, the area that hugs the City is now a playground for the post-work drinker. Each night loosened ties and kebabs hang off financial workers set free from the private zones that they had spent the day haunting. Liminal grey architecture, spooked into being and benefiting from an illusion of solidity. A frozen state. Business eatery hypertrophy inferring that the party is long gone.

A few years ago, Dalston didn't seem ready for the trickle up. But now? Dalston Square certainly seems to be. Flats built in a flash in the big push forward to Olympiad Year, 2012. Bought up by private landlords and rented to the cash-rich, time-poor. Preened professional networkers who bellow their credentials at you, glass in hand, in the upstairs room of a house party, and look scornfully if you so much as think about recoiling, each being an example of the adjective that was abused until it became a proper noun: "Creative".

Look up for long at the yellow brick and grey of Dunbar Tower and you can no longer see it. Eventually, in theory, the residents will never need to leave. They have been promised supermarkets (Waitrose and Marks, natch), a café and restaurant in the coming months and years. The CLR James Library and Hackney Archives. I contacted the latter. 'Dear Mr. Burrows... We are moving to a new building just opposite Dalston Junction overground station... I am not aware of much material on reggae in Hackney...'

FEBRUARY 1849: ELEVEN-YEAR-OLD JOHN MUIR LEFT DUNBAR AND SET OFF ON A JOURNEY WITH HIS FAMILY TO AMERICA. HE GREW UP TO BECOME THE WORLD'S FIRST NATURE ACTIVIST. HIS WRITING AND TEACHINGS HELPED CREATE THE NATIONAL PARK SYSTEM IN THE USA, STARTING IN YOSEMITE VALLEY.

Representation is all. Without a PR campaign that second-guesses the needs of your demographic, you're not there. Dunbar, East Lothian didn't seem to exist beyond Newton's pictures and the little I could find online. The contrarian impulse had kicked in – travel up to Scotland for no better reason than the fact of this sudden rush of blood.

I arrive on a bright Easter Sunday morning in Dunbar. A ragged greyhound leaps fitfully outside the public toilet (which has apparently won regional awards for its cleanliness, and does indeed have a female cleaning attendant seated outside it on a chair on Easter Sunday). An ex-squaddie in full camouflage kicks a deflated football high into the air. The hound chases it, such is its inclination. Down on the harbour, lobster cages are stacked with nets strewn over them, the property of topless fishermen who banter with one another in the not-quite-warm spring sunshine. At the water's edge, three young boys size up the brine momentarily, before walking in without a flinch, as if it's a corn field they're stepping into and not the North Sea. A child of no more than two-and-a-half, a miniaturised man with a full head of black hair, stands a reserved enough distance away from them, skimming stones like someone's dad.

Cromwell Harbour was constructed under the orders of The Protector himself. It was here that Oliver Cromwell's New Model Army had fought to ensure there was no restoration of the crown during the volatile fallout that followed the execution of Charles I. In 1650 Cromwell's forces defeated General Leslie and the Scottish Covenanter army. He took 10,000 local men prisoner. Three thousand were marched down to Durham; half died on the way; remains have recently been discovered in a mass grave outside Durham Cathedral. From the survivors, a battalion of almost 1,000 were shipped off to Jamaica. Of those who made it to the island, very few came back. They were slaves, white slaves, separated from the security of their daily lives to form an unwilling force for English interests in Jamaica. It was a one way trip that is recognised as the primary source of the Dunbar name on the Caribbean island today.

It's hard to pinpoint where the rocks end and what is left of Dunbar Castle begins: it grows out of the land as if it had always been this way, a geological occurrence, an unintentional quirk of the landscape. It was once a significant piece of Scottish defence, and a bolthole for royalty. Mary Queen of Scots was famously held captive by the Earl of Bothwell here. 'For 12 days he kept her at Dunbar Castle,' wrote Eleanor Hibbert under one of her many pen names, Jean Plaidy, in the 1963 novel *The Captive Queen of Scots.*

'His passionate mistress and his most willing slave.'

When James VI, King of Scots acceded to the throne of England to become James I in 1603, the castle became surplus to requirements. It has been at the mercy of neglect and the attentions of the wild North Sea ever since. Much was demolished to build the harbour, but still a hunk of stone juts out of the shore. Red bricks, locally-sourced, one on top of the other and surviving, just. A patchy white blanket of Kittiwakes covers the side of the ruin, but before you catch a glimpse of that, you hear them. Taking little brick notches as individual homes, they cry out to each other incessantly. A teeth-on-edge, avant-garde performance, atonal squawking colliding with unbearable, high-pitched squeaking. They have taken over, stubbornly clinging on to the remnants of a high-rise block that was partly demolished years ago and left to deteriorate.

Travelling south back to London from Dunbar, I take a detour via the Baltic Centre for Contemporary Art in Gateshead, a gallery housed in an imposing former flour mill that faces Newcastle on the River Tyne. In the main exhibition space is the work of the artist George Shaw. Anonymous suburban portraits of Tile Hill in Coventry, the area in which he grew up, using Humbrol enamel paints more often used for Airfix models. Abandoned buildings and fences. Block greys of garage doors, the ambiguity of the light-slate sky. Much fenced-off, closed for construction, titles such as *The Age of Bullshit*. Documentation of a majority landscape in Britain that, without the steroid injection of freak capital, has not been open for business for decades.

When the old mill was converted into a gallery in the mid-90s, kittiwakes that had made the building their home were deemed undesirable, and were rehoused in a specially constructed tower. They returned and nested on a terrace on level four of the building.

'[A] slender metal structure rehoused kittiwakes expelled when the Baltic flour mills were converted into a gallery in 1997,' wrote Martin Wainwright in the Guardian in May 2011. 'But 30 pairs of the resourceful birds have found their way back, and CCTV footage of their nests and fledglings is being used as a gallery attraction.'

JANUARY 9 1940: THE 10,002-TONNE SHIP *DUNBAR CASTLE* SANK AFTER HITTING A MINE SEVEN MILES OUT FROM RAMSGATE. IT WAS CARRYING EDUCATIONAL MATERIALS AND RACEHORSES TO BEIRA, MOZAMBIQUE. TEN LIVES WERE LOST AND ONE RACEHORSE WAS KNOCKED INTO THE SEA. EYEWITNESSES ATTESTED THAT BOOKS AND PENCILS WERE WASHED UP ON THE BEACH AFTER THE BOAT WAS SUBSUMED BY THE WATER. THE ONLY PASSENGER TO DIE, WALTER RUSSELL-JOHNSON, WAS LATER BURIED IN ABNEY PARK CEMETERY, STOKE NEWINGTON.

Newton Dunbar's thirty-three years in charge of the most put-upon club in London was a constant fight against the opposing forces that wanted to close it: the police and the council both aided by the certain sections of the media. The club was raided by the police on seven occasions. Newton claims he was taken to court 14 times for offences relating to the club, yet each time the charges were dropped. 'There was always a drama but everything was found in my favour each time,' he says, adding that he was repeatedly 'fitted up' by the police. 'On one occasion they sent a mountain of drugs that they had supposedly found in Four Aces to forensics. They were sent straight back. "Don't waste our time," forensics told the police. "The only fingerprints we can find on them are yours."'

It was therefore of the utmost importance that the proprietor kept control, so Newton looked into installing early CCTV technology.

'I think it must have been in the early 70s, when nobody else had thought of using it: not even people in very strong and advanced organisations installed CCTV cameras,' he explains. 'The pictures were shown on a television set that I had in my office. Everyone who came saw it. It was a tool and I knew what my responsibilities were: I had to be able to see things that were going on. In many cases it actually saved a lot of problems from happening. Too numerous to mention. People doing things that they should not have been doing. I was able to address these situations without a lot of fuss. Of course, in the end people knew it was there. Some had never seen anything like it. It used to be quite a discussed subject, to find out why I knew certain things had taken place.'

Newton's early implementation of CCTV was Hackney's unofficial motto in action: 'Control or be controlled'. He also customised his office so he knew who was coming to visit him, friend or foe.

'I had a mirror that was on a rail and it was over a window. A sliding mirror. When I wanted to look out the window I moved it along and I could look out. I had a door fitted behind a wall in a panel that led into an inner room. Nothing was what it seemed in there.'

Secret doors and hidden rooms, like something out of *James Bond*. Ian Fleming's fictional spy became middle class Britain's introduction to Jamaica before music did, and his love affair with the island turned the imperial colony into a desirable holiday destination for those who could afford to get there. It was influential on reggae too – Desmond Dekker's *007 (Shanty Town)* begat 007, another popular Dalston club near to Four Aces.

While Newton was earning his education in Montego Bay in the early 1950s, Fleming was beginning to spin out these boy's own adventures at his Goldeneye retreat along the coast at Oracabessa. In 1952, he wrote *Casino Royale*. He later bluntly described the process of writing his debut novel as being, 'Roughly the equivalent of digging a very large hole in the garden for the sake of the exercise'. In 1956, the year Dunbar left Jamaica for England, the Prime Minister Sir Anthony Eden, suffering from the after-effects of the Suez Crisis (effectively Britain's last act as a colonial power), flew in the opposite direction to recuperate at Goldeneye. He had been threatened from all sides and faced the possibility of Eisenhower pulling America out of the friendship that postwar Britain relied upon. It was an event that pin-pricked any semblance of moral authority that Britain still had over its Commonwealth, with Colonel Gamal Abdel Nasser standing firm against Britain's use of Egypt as a base from which to affect its powerful stranglehold on the Middle East. Empire by now only existed in the mind, so Eden rushed for the next viable alternative – fantasy, provided by Fleming, a man responsible for inventing what has since become a far more saleable figure of British power than Eden could muster: James Bond, the writer's prolonged daydream at the end of a life of imperialist adventure as a naval intelligence officer and bed-hopper.

Before he became prime minister, David Cameron, a fellow Old Etonian, ensured that his admiration of the James Bond franchise was communicated to the public. So much so that it became common knowledge that he had seen each film in the enduring series at least three times. Sections of the media have tried to buy into the connection, creating a new and very strange kind of myth of Cameron as a doughy-faced action man. 'The Prime Minister, looking as debonair as James Bond, was quick to undo his bow tie as soon as he stepped into the car waiting to whisk him back to Downing Street,' wrote the Daily Mail during the September 2010 Tory Conference.

Back in April 2010 the Conservative Party poster on Dalston Lane that bared Cameron's face had vanished, replaced by a message: 'OUR DREAMS DON'T FIT ON YOUR BALLOTS'. On TV, radio, online, everywhere, people were talking about televised prime ministerial debates, that brief dalliance before the prolonged punchline of government. The papers said things like: 'On Twitter, he won praise for his suit and tie.'

'It's a done deal,' says Newton as we stare up at the dilapidated terrace on Ashwin Street that is awaiting demolition. 'What is going to happen will happen. As Shakespeare said, "All the world's a stage."'

NOVEMBER 28 1991: DUNBAR BANK, A PRIVATE BANK SPECIALISING IN PROPERTY FINANCE WHOSE FOUNDERS INCLUDE SEAN CONNERY, OPENS ITS FIRST SCOTTISH BRANCH IN GLASGOW

When Newton Dunbar arrived in England in 1956 he sought to build a career in law, but inevitably got a job on the railways. That's the way it worked for incoming Jamaicans: men would work in transport, women for the NHS. Yet he fell in love with the romance of steam.

'I worked for them for well over five years,' he says. 'I got sucked in because working on steam engines during those days was a job that got into your blood. You started off with the suburban trains: from Kings Cross to Hatfield and Welwyn Garden City. After that you progressed to the bigger class engines, where you'd fire to places further afield, like Peterborough. In some cases you'd end up on what they called the mainline – you'd even go up to Newcastle and Scotland.'

Up the country and back down again, firing the engine, stoking the coals. The smoke, the heat, the repetitive rhythms – you might connect this love affair with steam to his later, longer relationship with the club life.

'When I started earning money I went to blues parties,' he says. 'You'd find out where they were through the grapevine. Then we started going to the clubs in the West End. There was one on Berwick St, owned by a Maltese bloke by the name of Gato. There was a café upstairs, and below that a basement with a jukebox. There were a lot of black American GIs, and teddy boys who used to go there. The GIs were the ones with the money. During those days they generated a lot of ready cash, selling cigarettes by the carton and bottles of whisky taken from the base they were stationed at. I used to leave straight from there to go to work the six o'clock in the morning shift.'

In 1962 the steam locomotives began to be withdrawn, and were replaced by diesel electric engines:

'Not everybody was keen on it. Most of the drivers and the people who were involved on the railways didn't like such a drastic change. The main problem was getting used to a completely different animal, which these electrics were. People saw the new machines as alien. It meant they had to re-train. They didn't really want to get involved with it but they were forced to and, of course, amid the moans and the disapproval, life went on the way it was organised for you.'

JULY 19 1795: FOUR UNFORTUNATE SOLDIERS WHO BELONGED TO GRANT'S FENCIBLES WERE CONDEMNED

TO BE SHOT AT GULLANE LINKS NEAR DUNBAR, EAST LOTHIAN FOR MUTINOUS CONDUCT AFTER TALKING BACK TO AN OFFICER. ONE OF THE MEN WAS REPRIEVED IN ADVANCE. ONE WAS PARDONED AT THE LAST MINUTE AFTER LOTS WERE DRAWN. AFTER THE REMAINING TWO MEN WERE SHOT, THE SECOND STRUGGLING FIERCELY, TWO CHILDREN COVERED OVER THE TRACES OF THE GHASTLY MORNING'S WORK WITH DRY SAND.

Newton moved to engineering, yet he had already been bitten by the intoxicating thought of running his own nightspot.

'There was a clique of friends who had met at the blues parties. We had this fantasy of owning a club, because it would come with all the trimmings of the time – music, money, cars, girls. We probably got the image from the American concept, picked things from the movies. Any Hollywood film in which the club scene was portrayed was imprinted in our minds and utilised to formulate this idea of what a club should be like.'

The opportunity to fulfill their collective dream arose at Aberdeen Park, near Highbury Corner.

'There were hotels and guesthouses around there, it was completely different to what it is like now. One guesthouse had a basement that was owned by a man called Mr. Weekes, like the cricketer. He was a Trinidadian gentleman. We approached him in 1965, I think, and were given the go-ahead. In the end we called the club Four Aces as there were four of us involved, it was also the name of a very popular brand of cigarette in Jamaica at the time. The three other guys left me to it in the end, and I eventually took the club to Dalston Lane.'

We cross the road to Dalston Square, to survey Dunbar Tower. Balconies behind glass, minute pockets of living; boxed-up plants, bikes, chairs and tables. The air, so often full of the dust and grit that puffs out of the gigantic building site of Phase Two of the project, seems suddenly fresher. The cries of gulls at Ridley Road, scavengers that come inland to pick at the waste left behind after the daily market, are only just audible above the wind that is starting to blow quite fiercely. These two places, Dunbar Castle and Four Aces, had seen it all and perished, and now we looked up at the outcome, this future ruin. Both were once sanctuaries of a sort. 'Places of refuge,' says Newton, 'but also confinement.'

21st MAY 2010: THE FIRST KITTIWAKE EVER RECORDED IN HACKNEY IS SPOTTED AT STOKE NEWINGTON RESERVOIRS. THE SIGHTING IS DOCUMENTED ONLINE. THE BIRD IS LABELLED "VAGRANT".

# The Battle of Kingsland Road

*By Paul Case*

*Excerpt from the pamphlet* **Retrospective Study of The Battle of Kingsland Road** *by Anonymous, p. 7, date unknown, publisher unknown*

*Just over a mile of traffic-choked concrete vein runs through Hackney, connecting two beating hearts of former mutual disdain. The North heart is called Stoke Newington, its beat slowly pulling in the lifeless Islington migrants east in search of fresh roots. Attracted by an itch to free themselves from the ties and prejudices of the middle class, then be soothed by a sensual scratch of underground chic. To them, it wasn't a London to be snapped through a camera lens and taken back to the provinces. It was a London hard and cold to touch, the air an invigorating smog. The teachers, the doctors, the businessmen, the youth mentors, the independent artists, the freelancers seeped in. The self-propped and the academic. Self-consciously dusty spines of Chomsky, Vidal and Sinclair snugged on antiquing bookcases. Red wine and spliff work wind-downs, cocaine smeared mirror weekend nights, dinner debates, hot, bored affairs. Rising rents.*

*Gleaming white paninis (smoothly bragging organic) began to nestle awkwardly against the artificial red, blue and white Americanisms of the Dixy Chickens, with their steaming brightness and their cheaply, deeply fried poultry. The pubs upped price. The indie rock leak from their speakers forming a cloud of sound that shadowed the estates and the tattered, homeless punks. There was surprisingly little tension between the new arrivals and the echoed concrete shouts, just a slow fading until only the well trained and newly bright remained.*

*You turn to face south. In the distance, The City's grey haze looms, the relic Gherkin centrepiece looming over the impenetrable Gucci banknote blur at its feet. You walk towards it, never to it, down Stoke Newington Road, to arrive at the border of Dalston Junction. Here, transparent high rise flats preside over Dalston's sprinkled, cramped trendy bars and Turkish coffee houses...*

*You walk just under a mile south to the next border. Shoreditch: formerly a crumpled slum, much like Stoke Newington, hollowed warehouses piled high, cramming in sweatshop workers and squatters. Whispered danger zones, blank blowjobs in alleyways, market traders. This enticed the film makers, the T-shirt designers, the drum 'n' bass producers who rapidly filled every space with exhibitions and the mangled electrics of blank grey laptops. Tossed wraps, with grained shards of MDMA stubbornly clinging, swept with the breeze.*

*A rainbow scene gestated. Skilled in absorbing rhetoric punchiness and regurgitating gaudy clenches of style. The fetishising of the nothing. Ostensibly the polar opposite to Stoke Newington's pseudo-intellectual liberal-left, it fashioned empty anti-capitalism and emptier offence. Pioneering extravagance.*

*Between these borders, The No Man's Land of The Battle. The choked vein. Kingsland Road. Afro-Caribbean hairdressers, bargain shoe shops with gaudy bright orange signs, subterranean Nigerian restaurants... This was the focus, the unexploded gunpowder keg...*

*For the new arrivals on either side of The Battle, it represented empty space to be coloured in. Primed to stamp their own locality brand, they began to charge. Things were going to change. One way or the other.*

***

*Manifesto of Stoke Newington's Rising Dawn, published in their online blog, web address not found.*

## STOKE NEWINGTON BROTHERS AND SISTERS

For too long, "gentrification" has been used in the pejorative sense. A word that describes the takeover and self-centred modification of underprivileged areas by the wealthy. We, Stoke Newington's Rising Dawn, are here to reclaim gentrification: not just as a word, but as a force. A force of righteousness.

Our growth thus far has been exponential; a natural, positive and peaceful movement. We have only the improvement of society at heart. But there are those who wish to stop us for their own self-serving ends. Brothers and sisters, we are under attack. Under attack from anarchist and leftist groups, with their glorification of poverty and philistinism, as if living comfortably and having a diverse range of arts somehow negatively impacts on Hackney.

More pertinently, however, we are under attack from the pretentiously (and erroneously) named Hoxton Liberation Army. They are our antithesis. Whereas we bring vibrancy into culturally undernourished areas, they bring garish, repellent fashion and meaningless language. Whereas we bring a pride in liberal, progressive ideals, they bring drunken arrogance in the form of the apolitical. They have transformed Shoreditch into a deafening blast of vacuousness, and now they have their sights set on Kingsland Road.

Kingsland Road is a strip of cultural nothing, ripe for colouring in. We need to stake a claim in this area, plant our flag with pride and joy before the Hoxton Liberation Army can plant theirs. If they get to Kingsland Road before us, they'll use it as just another cool, meaninglessly post-modern hang-out.

In short, the Hoxton Liberation Army wish to destroy everything we stand for.

Is this what our forefathers fought for? For the world to be sucked into the vacuum of anti-culture? For the torch-bearers of intellectual society to succumb to the likes of the Hoxton Liberation Army?

The politicians are useless to us. We must fight for Kingsland Road with our own steel. Fashionable pacifism has become redundant. We are willing to take up arms in this culture war, and die for our birthright. We must stand in solidarity against the enemy or everything we have worked for will be lost forever.

Kingsland Road must be ours.
Join the struggle.
Join Stoke Newington's Rising Dawn.

Signed,
Comandante Fisher

***

*A letter to Shoreditch-based* **Grip Magazine**, *issue 4, 02.11.20XX*

Honestly, what is wrong with these Stokeys? Don't they get that we'll win this? Clearly not. Because apparently they must have Kingsland Road. It's their "birthright". Oh, hang on, was that a quote? Yes, and fresh from their overwrought, pompous online "manifesto" (read: wannabe literati rant). Basically, it spends all its time ranting at us, with all the sweeping, ill-conceived generalisations you'd expect from bleeding hearted, sexually repressed liberals. It criticises us for having no culture. No culture? What'd you call the hundreds of pubs, clubs, bars, warehouse parties and squat parties in Shoreditch? The thousands of artists, exhibitions, dancers, DJs, musicians, promoters, producers and film makers? That is culture. So what if we steal things from other places? We just have no respect for artistic boundaries. We want to expand and progress! The Stoke Newington folk brag on and on about their "culture", and how we should all love and respect it blah blah blah. Yeah, I really wanna be part of a "culture" where you debate about books you haven't read over red wine and mid-tempo indie. Dead-end existence or what? Who wants Kingsland Road taken over by these self-satisfied cretins?

These cretins have also been responsible for the assassinations that have taken place in Hoxton Square. Only the other day, I was walking down the street, minding my own business, when BOOM – this snappily dressed lady and her toddler get their heads blown off by a sniper. Great eh? At least we have the balls to get face to face. What about the fight at Haggerston Station last Tuesday? We baited them coming out, and kept at them with the crowbars until the cops came. Three dead, didn't the papers say? Damn straight. The only good Stokey is a dead Stokey. And what about when we caught Henry Mallick trying to nailbomb the Cathouse Club? Or James Gordon? Or when we sprung loads of HLA members out of the Manor Road concentration camp?

We're coming out all guns blazing. We aren't the revolution. We are revolution, and when we've won Kingsland Road, we'll win Stoke Newington too, and beyond.

Militant regards,
HLA

P.S. P.H.A.T present DJ Skunk, Spastic Holocaust + MC Mao @ The Cathouse Club, 8pm – 6am. £10 entry, all proceeds go to HLA. Who's coming?

***

*Memo leaked from MI5, 07.11.20XX*

...The purpose of this new initiative is to discredit, sabotage and expose the two main opposing movements in the so-called Battle of Kingsland Road – Stoke Newington's Rising Dawn and Hoxton Liberation Army. We should focus on every aspect of their organisation – their leadership, their administration, their supporters and spokespeople – in order to neutralise them. We must follow them on a continual basis and exploit internal disputes and personal conflicts at every opportunity. Capitalising upon these is necessary in order expose them to the public as a dangerous threat. Attempts at recruitment must be frustrated. Co-operation with local governments and local media is essential, as they have the strongest links to the public. Through these institutions, we can control the information being imparted to the public. Every opportunity to ridicule and deride these groups through establishing these links should be taken advantage of.

The long-range goals of this initiative are:

1. Prevent coalitions between militant groups. We need to emphasise the political differences between these groups and exploit them in order to keep the revolutionary movement fractured.

2. Prevent violence on the part of these militant groups. Any potential troublemakers should be neutralised immediately.

3. Prevent the rise of figureheads within these movements, as they promote unification, martyrdom and a focus for revolutionary ideologies.

It is cautioned that the nature of this endeavour should under no circumstances be discussed outside of MI5, and that all necessary security measures are taken...

***

*A transcript detailing an exchange between alleged member of the Rising Dawn Brian Horley (32) and Rhys Jones (19), a member of Hackney Downs-based gang, E5 Boys. Rhys Jones was asked by unidentified agents to record the transaction in return for the deletion of his criminal record. Transcript taken 11.11.20XX*

BH:  Rhys?

RJ:  Who's askin'?

BH:  I'm Brian... I was asked to come and meet you for... the transaction.

RJ:  Transaction?

BH:  I... we... need... well, you should know...

RJ:  What?

BH:  Look, we need... guns.

RJ:  Why you askin' me?

BH:  I was asked to meet you here.

RJ:  You're not feds are you?

BH:  Feds? Oh,um, you mean police...

RJ:  Yeah. Feds. Are you or aren't you?

BH:  Um, no, I'm not.

RJ:  Let's see the coin.

BH:  Coin? I...

RJ:  The money, show me the money you pussy'ole. I gotta talk like you now?

BH:  No, of course not. I have the utmost respect for you, er, people. It's in my briefcase.

RJ:  Show me round 'ere.

BH:  Alright. There.

RJ:  That's a lot fam. You mans serious.

BH:  Yes, we are.

RJ:  A'ight. Get in the car.

*An open letter to MI5 and the police, published in* **Grip Magazine** *and The Stoke Newington - Liberation Army Coalition blog dated 17.11.20XX*

Dear X,

This is a brief letter to say one thing: your attempts to penetrate our movements have been pathetic and obvious. Typical divide and rule. Regent's Canal? Our "comrade" who turned up, face down in the water, left with only one eye and six fingers? That was just a warning. We can tell who's who. Any other infiltrators will be similarly punished.

The Battle of Kingsland Road was between Stoke Newington's Rising Dawn and the Hoxton Liberation Army. And now, thanks to your interference, our fight is with you. Because of your actions, your unwillingness to allow our fight to continue without your interference, we have now come to a truce. Enemy's enemy is our friend and all that. We have agreed what to do with Kingsland Road, and it is none of your business. And now we have turned on you. This is your opportunity to back off and leave Kingsland Road to us. If you don't, we cannot be held responsible for the bloodshed you will cause.

Sincerely,

Stoke Newington's Rising Dawn – HLA Coalition

***

*Excerpt from the pamphlet* **Retrospective Study of The Battle of Kingsland Road** *by Anonymous, p. 10, date unknown, publisher unknown*

*Late November, 20XX. The bars of Gillett Square had transformed into shelter, then into bunkers, finally settling as splintered, shattered, dead rubble. From the scattered newspaper reports, the hysterical eyewitness statements, the propagandistic pornography issued by all sides, the information we garner is this: at around 4pm, the sun high, bright and cold, there was a secret truce meeting. Police snipers ordered to open fire, get rid of this nuisance once and for all, a return to normality via clipped skulls. Armed police charged the building. Fire returned. It lasted two days.*

*Two days of smashed glass and bone.*

*Two days of clashed arteries and slashed silences.*

*Two days of trapped citizens moaning, helpless and unhelped, legs pinned under the bricks of collateral damage.*

*Two days of meddling, melding, morphing politics.*

*Two days of flustered, disabled, useless news.*

*Two days reductively termed rioting.*

*Two days of things...*

*... 'things', a word we use when we simply don't know what we should be focussing on. 'Things' are changed/are changing/are going to change. 'Things' are going back to how they used to be, after the uniformed/non-uniformed, broken bodies are cleared away, another buried chapter in history's graveyard, don't worry about it, it wasn't real as such, the violence is now cleared, everyone got it out of their system, just a bunch of rich kids kicking off, just the collective psychopathology that underpins the structure of our society erupting into tribal conflict, nothing to worry about. Forget it.*

*An email from scriptwriter Graham Irons to Claire Spence, head of Hallmark Films, sent 06.05.20XX.*

Dear Claire,

Thank you so much for your quick response to my original email, and for your enthusiasm. As requested, please find attached a sample of my screenplay for *Kingsland Road: A Battle for Freedom.*

I feel last year's events in Hackney would be perfect for cinematic retelling. It has everything full-blooded cinema requires. For example, it has perfect heroes in the form of the leaders of the Rising Dawn and Hoxton Liberation Army. Whilst at war against each other, a mutual, begrudging respect begins to grow which, by the end of the film, has turned into a lifelong friendship. The screenplay shows that, whilst The Battle of Kingsland Road was indeed a real battle, it was first and foremost a battle of the heart. This is emphasised by the love interest Mary Kelly (get the East London link???), the beautiful prostitute who represents the poor and needy, and is forced to realise that the affluent freedom fighters really do know what is best for her community. *Kingsland Road* has romance, full-blooded action, conflict and resolution.

Obviously, some aspects of the real battle must be excised for the sake of narrative. The torture and murder committed by both groups and the police, for example, confuses the ethics and will present too complicated a tale for mainstream audiences. Likewise, the attempts of local communities and anarchist groups to protest against the Kingsland Road takeover should not be included.

But I feel these are minor details which we can afford to exclude in favour of the bigger picture – the bigger picture being a beautiful story of love, loss, duty, forgiveness and, finally, freedom from oppression.

I see the film as *Battlefield Earth* meets *Secrets and Lies,* as directed by Spike Lee.

What do you think?

I look forward to hearing from you.

Yours sincerely,
Graham

***

*Excerpt from the pamphlet* **Retrospective Study of The Battle of Kingsland Road** *by Anonymous, p. 34, date unknown, publisher unknown*

The postscript is never-ending, constantly tumbling. Prominent members of the Hoxton Liberation Army and the Rising Dawn found in bathtubs. Dark, dank red, water and speckled white walls. Rumoured informer, Rhys, feet dangling in his bedroom. His mother constantly campaigns, often alone, outside Stoke Newington Police Station.

Cold machine-gun police now stride Kingsland Road constantly, patrolling the borders, severing the vein between the two hearts. Stop-and-searches on anyone looking vaguely white, vaguely middle class, vaguely affluent. If you're not guilty you've got nothing to hide. Hunched shoppers scurry, eyes down, thick fog hanging over them. Stiffened populace. Ignore the CCTV and FIT, the blank history-less newspapers. The more you ignore, the greater the chances things will return to normal. The dead are dead. You are alive. Be grateful they've spared you.

# Tara

*By Gavin James Bower*

Tara's spending another evening in Dalston.

She's on Cecilia Road, the public footpath that skirts round its edges – parallel to the astro-turf football pitch, adjacent to the new academy.

She's lying face up on a towel.

She's working.

The man brings it 'specially, as if he really wants to do it here – parallel to the astro-turf football pitch, adjacent to the new academy.

It's 4:03am, and he's ninety-six seconds in. Tara's counting.

Ninety-seven...

Ninety-Eight...

Ninety-Nine...

She thinks it's all over.

It isn't.

The morning before, things look different.

Ridley Road Market, crack of dawn. Pongs of meat, big style. Pig trotters and snouts – the lot – piled up in vats. All for sale.

Buys two plastic tubs: one peppers, one cherries. Way nicer than that shite they sell in Sainsbo's. Nods to the brown bloke with the sweaty palms. Moves on.

Walks down Kinglsand High Street next. Rammed as per. Crackheads gathering down from the Overground, picking on some little albino slapper with her arse hanging out – no shoes. She tries to do one but only finds a phone box. Thick cunt.

Gorgeous floral dress in the window of Oxfam, down from the junction. Like them flowers round that Lutheran church, on Ritson Road. Dead tempting.

Not today. Need to mind them pennies – or else wait for my Lord Sugar Daddy to come-a-knockin'. Might take out a personal, like. Can see it now:

Geordie lass seeks handsome, hung man – scratch that.

Geordie lass seeks hung man, with dollar.

Onwards. A day off – on a day like this and all. Sun out, no clouds neither.

She walks all the way down to Albion Drive, cuts across then to the Fields. Posh as fuck houses on there. Maybe one day, if she works hard.

Yeah, yeah. Pull the other one, pet.

MADE IN BRITAIN scrawled on a wall, opposite Colin the bike thief. Quick wink to one of her best customers. Even takes off his rings when asked. Lovely bloke. Proper sound.

Time for a coffee. Not in them poncey shops down the Broadway. It's a hop, skip and a jump across to Mare Street from here anyway. Pot of summat strong and black, please. Change from a fiver? More like change from a quid. Need to mind them pennies, remember.

Can't spot a bendy, so walks down to the canal.

Clocks a nice bench, inviting, with no one else about – apart from the odd cyclist, and the swans. Nice place to drink this, she thinks.

Plans the rest of her day, without a care in the world.

***

One hundred and one...
One hundred and two...
One hundred and three...

Distraction, that's the trick with tricks. She thinks about the way the bloke lays out his towel at the start – all careful, like he's on holiday.

Then she thinks about the money. She's careful, too – making sure he pays upfront. Last time she was on – not far, Shacklewell Lane matter of fact – he jogs on before coughing up. Head. Wall. Tara the twat.

Still at it so she looks to her left, the houses opposite. That someone watching? Fucking pervs, the lot of 'em.

Here's to another evening in Dalston, she thinks, making sure not to giggle. Don't want to put him off.

Counting and panting.
Counting and panting.
Counting and panting.

She counts, still.

# Neo-Noir Hackney Haikus

*By Brendan Pickett*

Uniform street moons
illuminate garbage men's
neon work of night


Square, fixed perspectives.
Hackney's studio voids of
red lights, empty space.

Graffiti nametags
peace mural of a brass band
markets reek of fish


Smokers talk book-talk
outside pub-doors exhaling.
Non-smokers warmer.


Buildings cough white steam.
Litter bags clutter high streets.
Jack Frost steals my bike.


One-four-nine light trails
streak round the common green patch.
Night-shift drunks stagger.

Warm fill of kebabs
through the nostrils, down to lungs
east-end's finest food.


Off-licence open late
tired Turkish coffee drinker
harassed by da yout


Gentrification.
Hearty homeless guy's hard eyes
asking for a smoke.


Public pissing point,
by silhouette market stalls.
Steam rises slowly.

Gated Academies,
artificial landscaping,
youth strangled with fear.


Mondrian offices,
abodes of middle England
stymie Hackney's sun.


Moloch's Art Deco
temple digests commuters
daily at peak times


"Sorry! No low rents."
Olympic Estate Agents
break record profits

Fashion boys-and-girls,
slum it with dad's luxury.
Dustman collect trash.


Gherkin horizon
looming over Murder Mile.
Better watch your back.

# Alevism and Hackney

*By Natalie Hardwick*

An account of Hackney today wouldn't be complete without exploring the omnipresence of the Turkish community. Their rich cultural identity, enveloped in a fierce loyalty for their kin, is everywhere to be seen, clustering around the hubbub of Kingsland Road. Of the 400,000 or so individuals of Turkish heritage who live in London – a figure guaranteed to rise with each Census – most fill traditional roles. Housewives, patriarchs, shopkeepers, restaurant workers, taxi drivers, mothers, fathers, and an aspirational new generation following in their footsteps.

As the population of Hackney changes in character, the creative sub-culture spilling out into council blocks and sports bars, no deep-rooted community seems to have adapted as well as the Turkish. A reciprocal respect is potent. I remember the first time a Turkish shopkeeper let me off with 50p. Hang on, I thought, London was an untrusting city of anonymity and cynicism. Turkish bars and restaurants have long opened their doors for the takeover of the DIY club nights and gigs, Bardens Boudoir a blueprint for so many to follow, Efes Snooker Hall being a pretender to the throne.

When the riots rocked our beloved borough on a Monday evening in August, many took a Blitz-like approach and battened the hatches. Many more were keen to be in the thick of the action helpfully stood back filming on their smartphones, android children of the Big Brother generation. The Turkish community came out in force, an infallible human roadblock along the Kingsland Road, infamously wielding kebab knives in one well-documented case. If they weren't to guard the neighbourhood businesses, doggedly built from nothing over decades, then nobody would. A Facebook campaign followed: Thank Turk It's Saturday. A slightly patronising ode to our protectors, nevertheless the sentiment was right. Their cohesive fighting spirit was exemplary and even better, executed naturally without a second thought.

Regardless, penetrating the Turkish community to learn of their history and conventions was a daunting task. I was ignorant of their culture, have a mother tongue of Northern colloquial, many many miles away from the rapid diction of the Ottoman Empire; a bumbling English woman. Why would they let me into their community? And how does one approach a huddle of boorish men gathering in Somine on Stoke Newington High Street at 3am, lit by the flicker of a football match? Or the strident women of the Turkish Food Centre, who shout across the tills under the lurid strip lights? Which business to choose? And it seemed a little churlish to just boulder in and blurt out, 'excuse me, are you Turkish?'

A safe bet for a starting point was the affable shopkeeper on Dalston's Richmond Road. As I gingerly asked of his heritage, he pointed to a red charity collection box, perched on the counter. 'Go here for everything you need,' he said, suddenly turning the whole encounter into something reminiscent of an episode of *The Bill*. I imagined myself sleuth-like, trailblazing into an underground bunker of Turkish figureheads, air thick with cigarette smoke, where everyone ignored me and continued drinking apple tea nonplussed. 'The Alevi Centre, they can tell you all about our community.'

Tucked away above TFC on Ridley Road Market, the Alevi Cemevi Centre is a doorway every Dalstonite would have passed and, for the most part continued walking. I crept up the sallow stairwell feeling like a voyeuristic Louis Theroux, Dictaphone clutched in paw. The room upstairs was archetypal community centre, but with the feel of a living room, sofas dotted around a plasma TV, screening an unintelligible satellite channel. The light was dingy, yes, but instantly comforting. Having phoned ahead, I was expectedly met by Cebrail Ozer, chairman of the Youth Committee, who swept me away for a chat while I dizzily attempted to soak up the warm atmosphere.

Cebrail and I set down with a cup of Turkish tea and he pluckily bounded into ambassador mode. As a voluntary coordinator, he is responsible for chaperoning a group of around twenty young adults during meetings. 'Being a Turkish youth in Hackney can often seem like a hopeless situation,' he said. 'A higher proportion of our youths go down the wrong path than those in other communities. As you'll know, this area has a disproportionately high number of gangs and drugs use, and Turkish teenagers can often fall into this. It's our job to help prevent this, meet up with youths from the age of 11, ask them what they want to do and help them with schooling.'

The centre, abuzz with kindred folk of all ages, provides a sanctuary for those practicing Alevism, a calm and secure place of conversation, learning and worship. The fact it overlooks Ridley Road, arguably the most culturally diverse example of Dalston life, seems appropriate. 'The centre is for Alevi people but the door is also open to anyone who wishes to come in and see how we practice,' said Cebrail. But to roll things back to basics, I asked Cebrail to explain exactly what Alevism is.

'Alevism is not a religion. This isn't a mosque, or a church. Alevism is a belief system, a way of thinking,' he continued. 'It dates back thousands of years to the area around Turkey and Armenia. It lifts from various religions: Buddhism, Muslim, Christianity.' So how do these age-old principles translate in Hackney 2011? 'Our main understanding is to always be good, never harm anyone else.

'If someone tries to hit you on the left cheek, make sure you turn your right one. Even if someone wants to harm you, you must respond through love. We believe in women and men's rights as equal entities. We live a communal life and have a strong social understanding. We see every ethnic origin as the same. Here in Hackney, there are so many communities, but we don't see ourselves as separate. Everyone is equal. The Cemevi is our centre, where we come to celebrate these ideas.'

As Cebrail spoke with conviction about his faith, I realised my whole community shtick was unfurling in front of me. Under the dog-eared plasterboard ceiling of the Cemevi, humanitarian notions of equality and fairness so lost in London were alive and well, being played out with sincerity. A knee-jerk reaction was to be dismissive. With religiously-tinged icons hanging above us, for a faith claiming not to be a religion, it certainly seemed that way. But what other religion promotes women's rights, and places its entire onus on forgiveness and expressing pure goodness? I wondered how there had come to be a tight-knit Alevi community in the middle of London without it passing into the view of most other residents, myself included.

'The reason why a lot of Alevi people arrived here in the UK from the area in and around Turkey is because we have suffered a lot of persecution over the years,' says Cebrail. 'There are political problems, as well as problems with certain religions. My parents left Turkey for that reason. They moved me and my brother when we were babies. A lot of people moved for the same reason.'

Many incoming citizens settled in areas where their forefathers had previously set up community centres, an example being the Cemevi in Dalston This softened the blow of the huge cultural transition, creating a crash mat of community figureheads and places to socialise. The vast majority of these Turkish and Cypriot Turkish nationals are based in London, clustered around the northeast of the city. Green Lanes, running from Manor House to Stoke Newington, is a particular hub. Having acquired businesses and bore children, the population is ever expanding

Within the London Turkish community, a large proportion is of the Muslim faith, devoutly traditional and of regular practice. They are catered for en masse. The Suleymaniye Mosque on lower Kingsland Road is a specifically Turkish place of worship. The first of its kind was the Azizye Mosque, which opened in 1983 on Stoke Newington High Street. The ornate building has an opulent tiled façade and stands incongruously among the kebab and mobile phone shops of the busy main road. Its inbuilt Halal butchers meant I often walked past and judged it to be a grandiose supermarket, maybe funded by a Lottery grant.

Among the Turkish, Alevis are a small minority, unheard of by many UK citizens. The UK Alevi Cultural Centres and Cemevi group place the number of Alevis in Europe at one million, with around 250 Alevi Cultural Centres in over ten countries, including Norway, Swizerland, France and Denmark. However, among the

Turkish community in the UK, Alevis are equally represented. Of the 400,000 Turkish people in London, there are around 200,000 of Alevi faith. Around 3,000 are members of the Cemevi in Dalston.

An entrenched history of conflict between Turks of Muslim faith and Alevis is ongoing in 2011. The back-story is blood-spattered and steeped in controversy. Alevi communities have been consistently victimised by right-wing Islamist militants through no provocation or reason aside from going against a conventional grain. In more recent years, eighty Alevis were murdered in Corum, Turkey in 1980, attacked by Islamic extremists; in 1995 an anonymous car opened fire with machine-guns on three Alevi cafes in a shantytown area of Istanbul. In a subsequent Alevi uprising, twenty-two people lost their lives.

Though much of this history is far displaced in the deepest corners of their homeland, Alevis in the UK are still acutely aware of being ostracised by their contemporaries. Even the young Alevi generation can regale stories of oppression. Cebrail introduces me to some members of his youth board. Although initially reticent, looking at me with sullen puzzlement, they eventually open up. Arzu Aldemir took me under her wing with a quiet maturity. The nineteen-year-old now lives in Edmonton, but grew up and studied in Hackney. Raised Alevi, she comfortably relayed the history of her faith. 'We have a lot of problems back in Turkey. Muslims don't understand our faith. They don't know why our women don't wear headscarves, why we don't pray in a mosque.

'Alevis in our homeland have been raped and murdered,' she continued. 'There are stories of babies being ripped out of their mothers' stomachs, houses set on fire, whole communities attacked. People can't understand the fact that we don't use a holy book and instead believe that God is in every one of us. When you look in the mirror, you see God. God is in the person standing next to you. We don't worship a higher force, we don't believe in Allah.'

Arzu is unassuming and speaks with remarkable ease about her faith. She is proud and knowledgeable, a glowing example of the new generation of Alevi youth. This generation not only live and breathe their faith and its admirable principles, but also embody those hardy qualities that only come from growing up in the whirlwind cultural cornucopia that is London: young wisdom, individuality and confidence, underpinned by ambition. Arzu has just got a new job, in a solicitor's office, and is a thoroughly modern woman, decked out in high street garb, dotted with silver like a jeweller's window display. She speaks in a charmingly piquant North London brogue.

Her best friend Burcin Akin inhabits the same traits. Her parents don't speak any English, having arrived in the UK from Turkey when she was a baby, nineteen years ago. Her mother stays at home and her father works. Like Arzu, she can speak, read and write in both English and Turkish having been exposed to both environments from birth. She too is ambitious, and proud of her lineage. 'In Alevism, we don't believe that men should be in one place and women in the other, like they do in Islam,' she says.

'That's why a Cemevi centre like this exists; so we can all gather together and talk as equals. Women can go around and do what they want, go with guys, have a drink, socialise, because that's what this generation should be like,' she asserts. 'We have a saying, "the end of the path would be dark if the path is not science". This relates to the fact that we have to constantly adapt, change and move forward with every generation. The idea of wearing a headscarf in the name of God is foreign to us. Our women have self-respect. If you act in a certain way it should be for yourself, and the way you want it to be.'

Burcin is at college and has aspirations to go to university. Cebrail too has been encouraged to aim high. He and his brother both went into further education. Cebrail has a degree in computer science. His father is a taxi driver and his mother a housewife, typical paths which the older generation of Alevis follow. Walking around Hackney on the hunt for Alevi-owned businesses, one would be surprised quite how many of their red charity boxes grace the counters of cornershops, off-licenses and cafés. Like traditional English families, the parents work to send their children onto higher planes, encouraging the new generation to push forward. The strong involvement of Alevi youth in the recent tuition fee protests pays testament to how they are by no means insular.

Beyond their non-traditional attitudes to aspirations and careers, the youth of the Alevi Cemevi in Dalston partake in traditional ceremonies. The *cem* ritual is a ceremony held weekly in all Alevi communities, and involves men and women gathering together under the motto "all for one, one for all". The ceremonies will often include a *semah*, a ritual dance – and the consumption of a *lokma*, a communal meal.

At one of our meetings, Arzu and Burcin encourage me to sit in on a ritual dance class. The group are preparing for their performance at the Alevi Festival, held in London each June. Thirty members of the centre of all ages swoop across the room, fluidly moving their bodies to a tambourine tap that renders the motion akin to a Middle England morris dance. As the group leader speaks in rapid Turkish, Arzu being unable to translate after being dragged by the hand into the troupe, the inner Theroux comes out as I sip a cup of tea smiling politely at the twee situation before me, desperately hoping I'm not asked to participate.

A Yoda-like bearded figure plays twangly folk from an unidentifiable stringed instrument in the corner, the faintly familiar sound of music played in kebab restaurants. I worm around on my chair unsure how to react, but I'm the only uncomfortable person in the room. I'm astounded by the sincerity of the teenage dancers, linking arms with buxom matriarchal partners. I eventually loosen up as I make sense of it all.

It seemed pertinent, but a little odd, that this quaintly traditional celebration was taking place above Ridley Road. True, to walk down its famous market during the day it is a swarm of faith, colour and creed. Gentrification as we know it in full swing. But a cohesive community is far from evident. People hang their heads, avoiding the gaze of those passing. Faces are ashen and weather-beaten, people with the weight of the world on their shoulders. Trolleys barging, elbows sharpened. Less communal vibrancy, more a test of will. So why were the Alevi youth partaking in a centuries old bop instead of standing with their arms folded in a surly sulk?

Half an hour into the dance routine and people's brows are beaded with sweat. Burcin and Arzu take an opportune moment to sneak out while Yoda's gaze is averted. We reconvene in a stairwell, where the girls smoke a cigarette in reassuringly teenage fashion. I'm bewildered but express my affection for what I'd just witnessd. Burcin explained what it symbolised: 'During the dance, when we were moving our arms up and down, that shows taking from the rich and giving to the poor,' she says. 'A lot of our practices pay tribute to our people and the act of remembrance and this is really, really important to us all. We say we forgive, but we never forget. That means we fast to pay tribute to the Alevi people who have died for our faith, the people who died with their heads chopped off, starving and without water.'

I'm surprised at how comfortably two teenage girls can discuss such a heavy subject matter. This is something they seriously believe in, not coerced by parents or peers. 'During our twelve days of fasting, we don't eat meat as it represents flesh. We don't eat onions as the act of chopping the round bulb represents beheading someone,' she continued. Arzu added, 'We don't chop anything during fasting. All vegetables, fruit or fish. If a dish requires something to be chopped we do it before the 12 day period. We can't drink water either. It's more intense than Muslim fasting.'

For a group claiming not to be a religion, the parallels between Alevism and the Muslim faith were glaring. With roots founded in Islam, the subsequent conflict between the two faiths seemed confusing, and something I discovered is by no means settled. 'Our identity is one that people are really unfamiliar with,' says Burcin. 'Alevism isn't taught in schools, not many people have heard of it. It was difficult for us to explain what we were as we weren't entirely sure ourselves.

'People would ask me "What are you? You don't pray and you don't go to mosque. You don't wear a headscarf. Are you a Muslim or not?"' she says. 'My young cousin still gets it now in school. There is no awareness and we can't be fit into a box. That's hard. We only knew what we were taught at home.' I asked whether they ever felt ostracised in school. 'No, I had lots of friends,' says Burcin, Arzu agreeing. 'I socialised with people from all backgrounds, in keeping with the idea that everyone is equal.'

This is a point Cebrail agrees on. He says that ten or fifteen years ago you'd see a lot more segregation between Turkish youths and those from other backgrounds, the same going for the wider community. Now there is better integration. Every generation to follow has blended in with its surroundings more effectively.

Burcin says this could be improved by more awareness from outside of the Alevi faith. Indeed, the internet is a mire of varying religious diatribe, expanded historical accounts and various blogs all referring to Alevism. But without being immersed in it, it is difficult to understand. You could be talking to a member of the Alevi faith every day, there is nothing to mark them out from anybody else in Hackney, aside from their Mediterranean-cum-Middle Eastern complexion. But the camouflaged doorway, ritual dancing, the crossed-legged sage... it felt a little like a "secret society".

To counter this conception, members of the Dalston Cemevi are keen to spread the Alevi message. 'There are no official statistics as we're not counted as a religious or "other" faith group. There was a campaign around the time of this year's Census among Alevis, urging people to tick the "other" box in the religious section, then writing Alevi. If we get 10,000 people doing this it'll be an option on forms in the future,' Burcin enthuses. 'Then we'll be on record so we can be included in the school curriculum. This will mean it won't be as difficult during school age as it was for us, the kids wont face the same prejudices. Once it's on the curriculum awareness is on the up.'

Once immersed in the culture of the Alevi centre and its members, I found the overriding common trait was a warm and familiar openness. Whenever I sat in the main room of the Cemevi, chatting to someone or other, people would flood to the table to introduce themselves, thrilled that someone was paying an interest in their cloaked faith. They were enthusiastic and keen to make the very best impression, always succeeding. During one conversation with the girls alone, about ten people of all ages gushed over to meet me, introducing a gurgling baby by a name I could never pronounce correctly, loveably cantankerous pensioners, young parents, all getting on together in fine fashion.

Despite us being individuals from opposite sides of the Hackney spectrum, I did feel a sense of us being kindred spirits on some level as it was difficult not to agree with so many Alevi sentiments. While communities can be segragated, protectively sticking with their own, when we're thrown together it often works. One Friday night I bumped into Seckin Akin, a twenty-year-old member of the Alevi youth board, in Efes Snooker Hall. Turns out his father owns the place. It was once purely a staunchly traditional Turkish haunt, but unfathomably and out of nowhere became an overcrowded Hackney hipster hangout. It's probable this is less to do with the 4am license and cheap lager than the fact that someone unofficially labelled it as "cool". It made me wonder whether being Alevi made you particularly tolerant of the new Hackney generation, who despite being a community of their own, are hardly inclusive.

I put this idea to Haydar Alus, a member of the Cemevi audit committee, responsible for fundraising and promoting awareness of Alevism. I said I was really surprised how welcoming people at the Alevi centre had been and how I in no way felt like an outsider. I said I felt I'd finally found the dying spirit of "community" right in the middle of Hackney. Being a woman left me vulnerable when carrying out blind research. I would never have even entertained the idea of entering a mosque or Caribbean barbers shop, both environments that are off-puttingly male. There have been no closed doors in the Cemevi.

Haydar beamed, saying I had just summed up Alevism. 'I'm so pleased you say that. We are welcoming. We accept people for who they are, no matter what race or sex. Everyone is welcome, whether you are good or bad, a sinner or not. The foundations of this charity are humanitarian. Yes, there are religious aspects but that's because we've been influenced by history. But we have maintained our core principle, which is to value human beings for who they are and what they are.'

He said there was no way I could fully cover the vast subject of Alevism in months, yet alone one article. The only way to understand it was to live it, he said. It is difficult to define the faith in words and even if you're born into an Alevi family it still takes many years to learn the practice. The highest level is 'wise one', a cultural leader. To get there you need to get through every bit of tolerance in life. It's not something to dip in and out of when you feel like it.

Haydar carried on relaying the Alevi principles. 'We have forty commandments. Including reliability, trustworthiness, honesty, practising good deeds, democracy, freedom of belief, equality. If we believe in a creator, then everything that has been created by him is part of God, therefore we are all God. Equality for everything that has life. Men, women, nature.

'We don't look at individuals. We say if one person in forty goes hungry, we all go hungry. Our folklore says that when our ancestors were starving they managed to make one grape feed forty people. That's how our faith works. We can live together as one,' Haydar continued. 'One thousand years ago Alevi men and women could sit beside each other in a room. Only two hundred years ago women were being thrown in rivers, accused of being witches in the USA.'

Haydar agreed with my notion that Alevis are suited to life in the UK, particularly around Hackney. They settled in the UK as they found it to be a very welcoming place. London is a great democratic Alevi hub. The laws, even if they're not perfect, allow for someone from Turkey or any other country to come over and settle in the UK with their family, build a community and enrich our economy and culture. The UK has created a safe hub for Alevism, something I'm proud of.

The people of the Dalston Cemevi intend to bring everyone together; people of Alevi faith and people from outside that. It has only 3,000 members but it's growing, slowly but surely. Haydar points at Arzu and Burcin. 'These girls are going to be the leaders in coming years. They are passing on the good faith. The only way to succeed and grow is by sharing and allowing other people, such as yourself, to come into our home. If we don't do that, we'd just be the same as a closed religion.'

When I took on the project of delving into the Turkish community of Hackney I blindly approached it with unbiased interest but fully expected the experience at times to teeter on the uncomfortably voyeuristic. And while I'd still be loathe to advise popping into the Cemevi to gawp at what goes on there, the Alevis who gather there take the opposite viewpoint. They taught me to loosen up, trust in literally leaving your door open for your neighbours to salvage, and embrace old world conventions instead of looking the other way or, worse still, snigger. It's hard not to run a Theroux-friendly fable-spouting voiceover before my end credits, but here it is: Love thy neighbour, forgive but don't forget and always abide by Yoda.


Thanks especially to Arzu Aldemir, Cebrail Ozer and Burcin Akin.

# III

Stoke Newington / Stamford Hill

# Pavel's Smokes + Fortune

*By Molly Naylor*

## Pavel's smokes

Friday night. Stoke Newington. Autumn.
Me and Pavel and Anders and Nyobi
serve over-priced cocktails
to well-refreshed city folk
who meant to go straight home after work.

We're understaffed
cause Ben called in sick
after getting bollocked on Monday
for forgetting to up-sell the Pinot Grigio
with the Jumbo Fish Platter.
This doesn't stop me
from dragging my feet –
work ethic is a notion
as foreign as my colleagues.

Pavel palms me a Lucky Strike
and we meet to smoke
behind bottle bins.
Silhouettes of strangers move into frame
I add a voice-over to make it film noir –
it's lost on Pavel
who exhales and points out
he can see the straps of my bra.

He tells me this month
he's made enough in tips
to pay for his brother
to get his teeth fixed
holds out his bottle for a clink.
I bitch about some change of shift
and barely hear when he admits
he's scared he can never go home again.

I think once, we kissed.
At Petra's party in January
and I imagine little half-Slav kids
as he trails ash across bin lids.

We discuss table 36 –
the woman in false diamonds
with maybe-fake tits
I diss the suits on 62
and share my theory
that we choose our social groups
back in school.

Pavel doesn't get it
so I ask about his country
was it like here, grungers versus townies?
He takes another drag, says that it wasn't
really like that at all.

He asks me why nobody here
likes Tony Blair.
There are gaps
in my teeth and my knowledge.
I think about the cutlery I have to clean
and hope I don't finish too late.

Pavel points out a rat
eating chips from a bin.
I bum one more smoke
from the hardest working bloke in Stoke Newington,
pull my knickers out of my arse
and go back in.

## Fortune

Hackney. Exterior. Night.
Dim streetlights in the low light
making Dalston look electric
as I clutch my credit card
immune to the boys
with the baseball bats.

On route to a party
don't stop me now
don't make me think
because as I wander with a warm can
to a house deep in the east of the city
I'm making dialogue from the way the sky
kisses warehouses pink.

At the party
there's a blocked sink
and we just laugh
as a red carpet
soaks up the stink.

There are no plumbers among us
nobody here knows how to put up shelves
somebody once said we were something
and we haven't forgotten yet.

Nobody here will become a teacher
and teach others how to teach.
For us, there is everything wrong
with a lack of glamour
and we're just finding out how far we can reach
how many pints
how many overdrafts
telling stories about our experiments –
the subtext that life will save us.

It won't.
But we don't know this yet.
Nobody asks, what if life doesn't save us
because every day
the market swells like a dying fish
every day we get a new MasterCard in the post
and a genie laughs –
that was your third wish.

A dim bathroom
lip-liner painted over pale, hungry skin
picture ironic dancing,
picture me, picturing him
(he could be anyone, but know
that there are job opportunities
in the cracks of his smile).

It is as if nothing can break
except dawn
and when it does –
the Gherkin watches over us.

Someone once said we were something
and we haven't learned anything yet.

*Extract from 'Whenever I get blown up, I think of you'. Reprinted with
kind permission from Nasty Little Press.*

# Tautologies

*By Gary Budden*

*Amy, twenty-seven, a charity worker, said: 'Everyone was looking beautiful in their trendy clothes. People were blowing bubbles and we had our guitars out.'*

– Taken from an article in *The Guardian*
regarding the London Fields shootings

## Prologue

A recurring image, perhaps plucked from a dream I once had, hits me from time to time. Staring at padded skull walls as trains shuttle me round the city. Standing waiting – smoking – for Anna. As I piss my poisons into filthy urinals.

London is ruined, broken. Derelict buildings lie shrouded in ice and compacted snow. A man with a familiar face stands somewhere on a glacial sheet in Hackney. It is dusk. With the ruins of the Empire behind him, a flare gun is fired into a darkening, polluted sky.

## 1. Foundations

*Modernise*
*Energise*
*Put up high-rise*
*Buy to rent*
*For young professionals*
*Yo-pros, don't you know.*
*Change the geography*
*Change the demography*

– Michael Rosen, *Regeneration Blues*

The cavernous opening to the new station on Dalston Lane inhaled and exhaled commuters.

The architectural nightmare of the newbuilds loomed high, a dystopian sci-fi warning spelt out in Lego bricks. They blocked the sunlight.

Gusts of human traffic blew out on to cracked paving, scattered, bolting for home, work, shopping. On the opposite side of the road, the Hackney Peace Mural shimmered in Indian Summer heat, its bleeding colours obscured by passing buses, their dirty grey exhaust trails spelling out obscure messages in the air.

I stood by the station entrance, dirty blue jeans and a black shirt bearing some out-of-date political slogan. Leaning against the wall as a group of school children scurried by, I sipped from a soft drink can and smoked a cheap cigarette. From where I stood I could see across Dalston Junction to where it joins Balls Pond Road, crowds of vehicles streaming by Celine's lumbering mastodons. I saw a man in a yellow frayed trench coat, with the look of an ageing punk, hand a package to a young man with shaved head and black boots. He addressed the young man, smiled, and strode off into the body-mass of Kingsland High Street, pushing through Turkish vendors. I watched him light a fresh cigarette. He disappeared into the throng and was gone.

Finishing my own cigarette, I crushed the ember beneath my trainer, checked my watch with irritation. Andrew, as usual, was late. I imagined some excuse involving not understanding how the new East London line worked, that he'd misread the timetable. Some joke involving the city's latest bit of "progress" skewing his mental map, knocking him off-balance. Part of the city's build-up for the great disappointment of 2012, the new line had connected Dalston, and by association Hackney, to the gentrified docks of Wapping, the hell of Canada Water, to the out-of-reach kindred areas of south-east London: New Cross, Brockley, and onto the hinterlands of Croydon. Bankers and margin-dwellers both no longer needed to travel through the centre.

Whilst waiting and draining my can, I thought of the last time I had seen Andrew; I had been out of the city for two weeks, family visits in Kent and South West Wales. Exiting that green lung I had returned to the metropolis, leaving behind the stories my grandmother told of people I had never met, my mother's tendency to drift off mid-sentence, her different trains of thought colliding with each other with messy consequences. I re-read a Niall Griffiths novel on the train home, listened to an old Icons of Filth discography. Tried to be site specific. Stig, the Icons' front-man, died in Hackney.

Mutual friends of Andrew and mine were ensconced in a squatted building somewhere off Mare Street. We had promised to go down and help, maybe even see if the place was feasible for parties, gigs, see if we could contribute. My enthusiasm had been waning lately for such things, but I wanted to get back into it. Missed the camaraderie, the sense of belonging, sometimes.

***

There is an underworld that exists in the places others say are worthless, abandoned, no longer viable. Life hides in fissures, the cracks, the gaps. I took a certain uncomfortable pleasure in the knowledge that my lifestyle, or at least a part of it, would be considered by some as worthless and pathetic. Derided as left-wing posturing, or the sad trappings of an adolescence that really should have been let go of. A figure of fun to be laughed at, without chance of comeback, on *Top Gear*.

There was pride to be had being part of the unwashed vegetarian hordes that terrorised the mental landscapes of the British Right, haunting the pages of *the Mail*. Littlejohn's masturbatory nightmare. The people whom they said didn't care about England, well, we are England, as much as football thugs, as much as blue-rinsed old ladies, as much as pub lunchers and corporate cocksuckers. The England I tried to represent was a place I was not ashamed of. Farmers markets and focaccia were not a substitute for culture.

Andrew had yet to arrive. I put in my earphones, hit play on my MP3 player, and a raucous track kicked into life. "Our Inheritance". It sounded good today.

Some months ago now, somewhere around Newington Green, we'd been to a party. A place invisible to the outside world. Wandering between different rooms, assailed by the sounds of different subcultures mingling. Klezma, dubstep, punk, reggae, drum and bass, hip hop. The sounds of The Other, of the real world, forever and always.

Perhaps, I was romanticising. I have the tendency. There, Andrew, his mind elevated on a mixture of uppers and psychedelics, had begun spewing all kinds of quasi-mystical shit. Stuff about Green Men, giants, ley-lines, the occult. I figured he had been reading too much Alan Moore, too many Hellblazer comics. He linked the Green Man, Robin Hood, General Ludd, Cernunnos, the Spriggan sculpture in Crouch End, then made light of what he was saying by mentioning sweetcorn and the Jolly Green Giant. I had been too preoccupied by a young woman to listen, sex heavy on my mind. I'd palmed Andrew off on some friends, then failed to get laid.

The next song. A tale of Irishmen shipped out to the penal colonies. Another cigarette lit.

\*\*\*

Immersed in the alternate-lore of the city in which I live, I feel myself to be a part of it in some way. An obsession takes hold, a compulsion to tease out the true stories, real histories, the myth and legend that suffuses everything, the personal biographies that saturate the pavements. A swamp of spilled blood, shed tears, lives forgotten then crushed beneath the wheels of progress as the city lurches ever forward.

On certain days, the revenants that hang sadly on street corners, or sit staring out of rain flecked night-bus windows, outnumber the living. Andrew and I bonded over this shared worldview.

Plus drugs, alcohol, punk rock and an aversion to working.

\*\*\*

More commuters tumbled out onto the street. They looked harried, keen to be elsewhere. Another cigarette was smoked down to the butt, tossed among dust and crinkled crisp packets. Andrew still yet to arrive. The next track began. An updated version of an old Ewan Macoll song. Brief thoughts of gypsies down in Hackney Wick.

A three month haze was lifting. A legal substance had been banned, become scarce, due to right wing media pressure. Secretly I was glad. Coming out the other side of it, giving my head time to breathe and to recover, I saw a fact that unsettled me. Cheap and plentiful, decent highs, but it had been too much – it had become commonplace, taken as a given, never-ending. I must have lost a week's worth of sleep. No wonder Andrew had been talking of seeing Green Men in the Lea Valley. The changing weather had brought with it break-ups, violence, tears and days locked alone in bedroom prisons. The sea change was palpable; move with it or go under.

I felt a tap on my shoulder. The music still banging in my ears, I looked into Andrew's face as he mouthed something at me that I couldn't hear.

'What?' I half-shouted, removing the plastic headphones. The rumbling drone of Dalston rushed in to greet me. I could hear a woman shouting at her child, a scooter buzzing angrily by.

'Ello mate! Where we going to then?' Andrew's Essex accent, faintly annoying today.

Abutting into the street, he seemed unaware of the annoyed looks he was getting from commuters forced round his tall frame. Military green shorts, a Conflict T-shirt that may have once been black, battered canvas trainers. He clutched a slim volume in his right hand. *The Lowlife* by Alexander Baron.

'Where'd you get that?' I asked, curious, pointing to the book.

'Bookshop down the road. You recommended it to me, remember?' Andrew smiled as he said this, slightly bemused.

'Don't remember. Anyway, we're walking down that way.'

I jerked my thumb to the right, toward Hackney Central.

'Can't we get the bus?'

'You're a fucking lazy git.'

*Laughter.*

More people billowed out of the station's mouth, onto the pavement.

## 2. Manannan Weeps

Dreadlock was talking about the Scottish band Scatha, green anarchy and eco-hardcore. Songs of crying psychopomps and Celtic sea deities seemed appropriate given the recent corporate oil disasters that had coated the headlines, before ebbing away from public consciousness. Clichéd metaphors of a bleeding Earth too much to take. Blackened and shimmering pelicans covered in earth-blood were powerful symbols, I thought, as I nodded a half-interested nod and tried to listen. With Buckfast-slurred syllables, the story was something about seeing Scatha in an old squat somewhere way Up North. 'Buckfast: Brewed by monks, drunk by punks'. It gets you fucked-fast. Smiled as I ran these puerile rhymes through my head.

Usually I liked to listen to these stories; it all added to the secret history in my head. I could play-act at being some arcane defender of repositories of hidden knowledge, forgotten and mouldering. I felt it was the lifeblood of the people (I was romanticising again). Scatha, the Worm. The shadowy Scáthach, the warrior woman, was the teacher of Cu Chulainn. Hardcore. Squats. Punk rock. Green activism. It all connected, a knotted tangle of fibrous information that one day, I hoped, I might untangle. For now I was still out in the field, a DIY anthropologist. Partly modelled on a mad historian from Maureen Duffy's *Capital*, drenched in new historicism, anarchism, punk rock, green issues. A nose-breaking punch thrown in a Mare Street squat linked to the routine of a local comedian and talk of "Sacred Clowns", to Machen's nightmare-paradise Stoke Newington work, *N*, to Sinclair's insane psychogeographies. The all-embracing Mother London that Moorcock so loved, the pounding drum and bass and dubstep of the warehouses in Bermondsey and the novels of China Mieville, a spider god, a TV series named *Neverwhere* with that guy from *Peep Show* in it. Troglodytes that existed in the forgotten stations of the Underground, an ancient stone weapon that struck down a wealthy man on London pavement, the Little People of the Welsh hillsides. Police batons cracking the heads of peaceful Climate Campers, Stockwell murders, an attempt to detonate Greenwich observatory. A heart of darkness right on my doorstep, Conrad convalescing in Dalston, a hospital now dissected and split into affluent nests. My circular trains of thought that began and ended in Hackney.

Dreadlock's story, however, was doing my head in.

We had entered the decrepit building half an hour ago, an old warehouse. Andrew was chatting with a guy he knew, someone with one of those stupid false squatter names. This guy shared a moniker with a monstrous sea-being from Jewish mythology.

'Is he Jewish?' I asked Andrew, later.

'As the Pope' was the reply.

I recalled the crestfallen look of a girl accused of having "squatter chic" by Andrew, and I laughed. Dreadlock gave me a strange look, then continued his rambling narrative. I wasn't sure I wanted to return fully to this after all.

### 3. City on a River

Always the city. Anywhere, everywhere, related to the city, the river-squatting deity whom I loved without question. Benevolent dictatorship. I paid fealty with my time, my patience, my sanity. An unequal power balance where I was always the supplicant. An amorphous changeling that I called London, an idea pinned to pages, ultimately unsuccessfully, by a thousand different scribes. Writers had trapped me here, handing me a puzzle that I knew I was doomed to never solve (but then that was part of the fun, right?) They prevented me from leaving, sunk me into a quicksand of fiction. I would walk streets mapped by words and painted by sentences. Willing it all to mean something. Anything.

A dialectic pulled me in two directions, kept me in the city, yet still there was longing for wild spaces. I read Blackwood's *The Man Whom The Trees Loved*, understood the man taken by the New Forest. When I visited my mother in a seaside town on the Kentish coast, now fashionable and thronged with boutiques and olive vendors, I would look at an old photograph from those close-yet-distant pre-digital days. An image of my younger self, standing with my younger brother somewhere near the summit of Mount Snowdon on a cloudy day, seventeen years ago, foggy memories. A picture that twisted my insides, and I knew I had to be back up that mountain, looking down as buzzards and ravens flew below where I stood. Something thrilling in that sight.

But I was here, in the city, a concrete straitjacket, a polluted and filthy crush of humanity. Constant low-level threat even if you chose to ignore the tabloid headlines. A thousand words hanging in muggy air, yellowing phlegm clinging to pavements, revenants of past hopes crowding the Job Centres, the weight of history sinking England into the indifferent sea. I know that one day the Thames Barrier will break, burst, and London will become a drowned world. Bring it on. Sometimes I stand by the Lea, see it teeming with undines and grindylow, feel the urge to plunge in and join them. Drag me down. Please.

## 4. Snow and Springtime

Andrew was keen to go ahead putting on shows and events in the squat. I was flitting between commitment and indifference. I was trying to mix more outside of the immediate circle, felt tired from vegetarian arguments and undiminished anger. How many times can you explain your position? The circle I had drawn around myself for protection had become a noose round my neck. At times I hated the things I loved and everything that had once set me free now wouldn't let me go. Andrew never seemed to be afflicted by such thoughts. Or at least he never spoke about it.

I was taking my relationship with Anna more seriously. Thinking about place, where I lived and interacted. Realised this was a place that I had, in some small way, already made a stamp upon. I wanted to stay with it, go the distance, put off the flight to the Commuter Belt until the ice came and forced us out. Andrew was talking about setting up some party, scoring pills and coke, sipping on his mid-afternoon pint as we sat outside a pub on Stoke Newington High Street. Déjà vu. Traffic screeched and squealed, the banshee's wail of a police siren sped past, young mothers battled for pram space with the fruit vendors. The same as always and endlessly new.

As Andrew talked on, I lost myself in memories of:

Carrying bags of vegetables back to the house with Anna, purple spouting broccoli, Jerusalem artichokes, red kale. Rooting through our cookbooks, tapping questions into Google, creating a new meal every night with what we had. The romance of the everyday, rooted in a specific location. Our postcode love affair.

'Sorry mate, what were you saying? I drifted off there.'

Andrew eyed me, briefly disappointed. He drained his pint.

'So I'm saying, we gonna run with this thing? I'll do most of the legwork, if you could help maybe booking a few acts, help with the promotion and all that…I know you don't wanna be as hands on as before.'

My face reddened. I fought the urge to break eye contact.

'Yeah, cool, let's do it.'

\*\*\*

When the snow and the ice came, it covered Stoke Newington Common so close to our home in a frozen pause. I skidded in inappropriate footwear. Anna slipped cartoon-style and ended up on her arse. We laughed, went home, drank tea. The city breathed, caught its breath and then the thaw came. But with us, at least, some of the spirit of those days remained. Remembered the ironic freedom of transport in chaos, the joy of workers and school kids alike streaming down the hill in Springfield Park on tea trays, sleds and bin bags. The thaw came and things went back to normal, but we remembered.

\*\*\*

Andrew looked happy at my response. I felt myself settle into where I was, preparing for a few more pints. We texted, phoned, gathered a gathering who arrived in ones and twos. A few hours later, we made the decision to move on to the next drinking hole.

I could evolve, with bridges intact behind me.

## 5. Utopia

*"Nostalgia is what happens when you don't do shit for years."*

– The Ruby Kid

Nineteen eighties echoes reverberated through the city. An exercise in nostalgia played out on flatscreens as the viewers at home laughed at footage of Mohawks in old Islington squats, and the spirit of Greenham Common was invoked with a mixture of affection and youthful folly. Zounds and The Mob squatted Hackney, on Brougham Road, in the eighties. The peace mural went up in those days. Days before I lived here. *Vice* magazine claimed to be following the DIY punk spirit, interviewed Oi Polloi, and I could only laugh and sneer. Was it better to ignore the Nothing, shrug it off, or to attack? I did nothing. I was worse than those who didn't care. Paralysed, pulled between war and capitulation.

The talking heads now seemed to know better, had made amends with their younger selves. Times change. Billy Bragg talked about the miners struggle. An official face of dissent that made my mum smile and dad consider listening to *Back to Basics* again. Gender politics and "man-hating lesbians" were talked about with a certain fondness. An ancient Ian McKellen was trotted out, with no mention of Derek Jarman and *The Last of England*.

## 6. A Piss in the Ocean

*"I am: yet what I am none cares or knows,*
*My friends forsake me like a memory lost;*
*I am the self-consumer of my woes"*

– John Clare, *I Am*

I look at my reflection. A reversed image of a man out of time and out of place, and I observe the shoes I wear, the rusting badges that cling to my green army jacket, the cropped hair that is growing out and the beard in need of a trim, the scar by my right eye, the t-shirt sporting the name of a band perennially unfashionable.

Grow up.

The world surges forward outside the window, yet some things never seem to change and I consider that sometimes the trends and clothes mutate but the times I live in (that I have no choice but to inhabit), the way my friends and I talk about things, they sound like a pathetic echo of the words my father spouted, perhaps less articulately, thirty years ago, and then I think maybe that's alright because sometimes there is no shame in nailing your colours to the mast. I'd rather go down believing than accept "the way things are", becoming a tacit apologist/supporter of things I know are not really right.

Certain issues do matter. We feel so free to express ourselves online, via news-feeds, updates, digital posts. But these are merely commodified feelings. We become more trapped and codified than we once were. These days people back off from sincerity for fear of embarrassment but... fuck it.

Better that than the alternative, the alternative that is no alternative at all, a gaping black hole of irony, invincible, destructive like the Nothing, I think in an absurd thought taken from *The Never Ending Story* (the tortoise terrified me as a child). Then I think of a comedian who said 'the last taboo is doing something sincerely and well'. Yes. My own image stands there in defiance, looks at me in challenge. Can I go on for ever like this? When is it time to give up, make peace with the lattes and ciabatta, the *G2* and treating life as a spectator sport. I stare at an unfamiliar figure in smeared glass, and realise I can never let some things go. Realise I will go down, believing, and be damned for it. A sea-mink swimming in Hackney Brook. A thylacine padding across Hackney Downs. A passenger pigeon in Springfield Park. Huddled in a shelter made from books that no one now reads. My colours were nailed to the mast before I'd even realised.

## 7. A Public House

I sit in our favoured public house, somewhere between Stoke Newington and Clapton. It feels half-visible and has a different feel from the ale houses that clutter the high street, for better or worse. Everyone is here. The gathering from earlier has swelled and expanded.

Andrew, calmer now but still prone to talk of squatting and the Green Man, says to me:

'You need to calm down. Learn to have some fun.'

He's probably right. Wandering too long in a haze of my own obsessions. I gulp at my pint, and it tastes clean, crisp.

Anna, sits opposite me. She looks good, if a little tired. She looks at me as if she hasn't seen me in a long time – happy, but cautious.

She says, 'You were losing the plot a little there. You don't have to be so angry all the time. Not everything is a battle, and these people you claim to hate, well, you're a hypocrite. They're not all bad. Not everyone cares about the things you do, that doesn't make them bad people.' At this she laughs, and I try to take it in the spirit it was meant.

'You know we agree with you, but just sitting and moaning, doing nothing, well, what's the point?'

She's probably right.

There's a big group of friends and friends-of-friends out tonight, and I feel happy. I walk without a chemical crutch, for a few hours at least. Part of me wants to get fucked up. Most of me does not. I want to wake up normally tomorrow, with my partner. Go look at the auroch skull at the Museum of London, eat a Turkish breakfast, read the paper, walk along the river. Something like that.

Anna, Andrew and Andrew's girlfriend are talking about when they saw Asian Dub Foundation. They are right, it was a good gig. I'm now in a conversation with my friend Ciaran, I've known him since school, and we talk of maybe nailing some of these ideas we have down on paper. Maybe as a form of catharsis, to get our voices heard. To do something. Anything. Everyone craves a little bit of recognition, even if it means being hated. We talk for a long time, downing London Pride, affirming that our voice is real, has meaning, exists. Too easy to be alone, locked inside your skull, with only a book for a bride. No need. A bit of honesty is needed from time to time, not anger. It is time, we decide, to turn some of this frustration into something productive. We take our inspiration from ourselves, our surroundings, our favourite writers, the fact that we want to do something. That, in itself, is enough.

Andrew and Anna's conversation must have changed course, because he interjects between Ciaran and myself, saying 'Remember when the fucking Restarts played in this pub?'

And I do.

It was a while ago now, pissing down outside, a truly torrential downpour. For reasons I forget I'd walked up to Clapton Common first, through the blackhats of Stamford Hill.

Then down Upper Clapton Road, turning onto Amhurst Road, the rain washing me clean and a sense of timelessness in the air. The few people on the streets scurried by, some holding the free papers over their heads in vain hope of abating the downpour. I got to the pub, entered. Andrew was there, met me with a grin. 'You're fucking soaked,' he shouted over the noise, laughed. Anna wasn't with me as she didn't care for punk music. The gig was good, a packed crowd in this little pub, steaming from the rain. They played *N16*.

These kind of nights, I reflect, occur with less frequency now. It will always mean the world to me, but we evolve.

Afterwards, I had crawled into bed with Anna, braving the rain again to get to her leaky Victorian house. 'You smell of booze and fags,' she had murmured before returning to sleep. It was a good night.

So I shout back to Andrew, 'Yeah, I remember.' Anna rolls her eyes in mock disdain. Ciaran now on his mobile, shouting something incomprehensible to his girlfriend who is, apparently, lost somewhere near Rectory Road. I get up for the bar, buy everyone a round. London pride.

And while I'm at the bar, I turn to look at Anna, my friends, the heaving pub. Tonight, the world seems full of possibility.

There is, always, a future.

## 8. A London Fiction

Andrew's squat party is in full swing. I am glad I have helped, contributed, am a part of something that is Something rather than Nothing. Dreadlock is here and he seems alive, interesting, tonight he's a walking piece of history and I am happy to listen to his meandering narratives that jump through time and across geographies with effortless ease. The trenchcoated man, whom I had glimpsed months earlier at Dalston Junction approaches us as we converse, he mutters something into Dreadlock's ear. The old punk laughs, Trenchcoat ignites a fresh Bensons and is off again into the crowd. Anna is here, in this derelict building; somewhere off with two friends sweating out the week's worries to drum and bass and dubstep, small revolutions of the self that demand dancing and release. Arthur Machen had suggested that a fragment of primordial creation lay somewhere in Stoke Newington: On nights like this one I think the dead Welshman was right; one room hums and shifts to the battle sounds of ska and punk rock, sweat misting the unofficial, un-approved air. Smoke clouds, dancing silhouettes, beings broken down to their constituent parts, the seething surplus moving in tribute to gods older than the ones you think you know, they dance against Mammon for a fleeting while, and they have a fucking good time.

I came here tonight via the Hasid enclave in Stamford Hill, thoughts turning to Alexander Baron, *The Lowlife*, the Jewish Hackney that fascinated in its absence, Pinter and Emanuel Litvinoff, their creations vivid and timeless, and how in some small way they relate to our lives now. Yiddish phrases still heard on some of our streets. Andrew's squatter friend with the mythological name walks by, I don't say hello, but tonight there is no threat from Leviathan or Behemoth, the apocalypse is on hiatus as long as the conversation keeps moving, the silhouettes keep dancing and words still fill the air. I bump into a Swedish girl I know, we chat and exchange stories. Belief, activity, will keep the serpents ocean-bound, the wolves that chase sun and moon forever on the move. I look at a group of late teens, furtively smoking and they're slightly wide eyed, buzzing on speed most likely, but clearly excited about finding this place. They don't fit the story, resisting the demographic internment camps. They are not sound-bites, nor broad brush strokes.

The night goes on, for ever.

***

## Epilogue – Tautologies

I will say the same thing, using different words, until the thaw comes. London is broken, ruined, with derelict buildings laying shrouded in ice and compacted snow.

Words become distress signals, flares, signs of life in a world gone cold.

I will continue to repeat myself until someone listens.

Then I can put this story to rest.

# 2061

*By Ashlee Christoffersen*

Rosa handed the ladle to her *compañera* and best friend Ana, shushing her as she did so.

They were nearly finished working for the day, when they would head to their small house on one of the farms surrounding the Boss's acreage. No, not 'their': the house and farm belonged to the Boss. Rosa had inherited the lease from her mother. In exchange, Rosa and Ana worked for the Boss three days of the week, giving him a portion of their farm's products.

The whole of the Boss's estate sat inside an eight-metre barbed wire fence in Stamford Hill. Similar sized estates surrounded it, broken only by wide roads, used mainly by large trucks that transported goods made and used on the estates, including the near-finished cooking oil that Ana was now stirring.

The Boss had been angry all afternoon. The young men had been here again today.

Rosa and Ana didn't know why the men had come. They had not entered any of the main buildings, the Boss's buildings. They'd come up the drive and spoken with the first of the workers that they had come across, the guards. One of the guards had left and spoken to the Boss. The Boss had stormed down to the men, gun in hand. The men had fled.

The first time the men came, Ana had suggested to Rosa that they try asking the guards what they had said to have so angered the Boss, though they both knew that would be difficult. The workers were kept separate, only encouraged to speak with their small "teams" (allocated by the Boss to those who did not have children) with whom they worked and lived on the small farms.

As the sound of the Boss's footsteps faded, Ana resumed, 'Let's go to the guard team's house, tonight, after Lights Time.'

Lights Time was 9:30pm, after which no one was permitted to leave their house. The Boss said that this was for all of their protection.

'Alright', Rosa agreed. She was curious enough to take the risk. Most often, she and Ana had managed to avoid capture leaving their house after Lights Time.

When they were caught, the punishment was severe.

\*\*\*

At ten o'clock that night, Rosa and Ana crept along the narrow cement path from their small farm, past eight other farms, until they reached the guard team. The journey there was slow. They flattened themselves to the ground each time the roving floodlights edged near enough to expose them.

The houses on the small farms had been built to look exactly the same as one another. They were one storey and made of brick, with a small front room, kitchen, shower room and a large bedroom capable of sleeping as many as made up each family or team. Each farm was distinctive, however. Households selected different things to grow to sustain themselves, trade, and to give to the Boss. Rosa and Ana grew enough wheat, fruit and vegetables to eat. They also grew varieties of potatoes, which they used to make potato starch, and vodka. They gave one third of their year's produce to the Boss. The rest they traded with the other workers.

Hearts beating from their most recent brush with the floodlights, Rosa and Ana finally reached the guards. The house was dark enough to make it appear that those inside it were asleep, though Rosa and Ana were sure the guards would be awake. They walked softly around to the right side of the house, to a small window between the front room and kitchen. Ana tapped lightly on the window, meeting Rosa's eyes with a small smile.

The face of Philip appeared at the kitchen window. Rosa looked at him with eyebrows wide apart, face open to indicate she had come for friendly reasons.

Rosa had known Philip, though not well, for a long time. Rosa had lived on the estate all her life. Philip had always been there too. But Philip was much older than Rosa, one of the oldest of the workers. One of those who could remember things being very different.

Ana had arrived at the estate just five years ago. Before that she had worked not far to the south. After the last person in her family had died, she took the risk of leaving.

When they met she had explained to Rosa, 'I had almost no information about the world outside of my estate, what the other estates were called, whether there were any houses available to lease or to live in, in exchange for working.'

It was believed that there was no free land that had not been enclosed into an estate. A few workers left estates all the time in the hope that there was somewhere.

Those that did risked their lives also because they were likely to be skipping out on a debt – there were very few who were not in arrears with Bosses, for having bought essential goods the estates were sometimes unable to provide. Bosses were not kind to workers who bailed on their debts.

This lack of information was in spite of the phones, computers, and televisions on the estates. These, senior workers could access without much difficulty. There was simply no centralised information production. No mass media.

Those like Rosa, born on the estates, only knew that things had not always been this way from the stories of Philip and the other older workers. Rosa was unable to feel the losses that were plain on his face, when he spoke of the times before.

Philip had shared his knowledge, limited and particular though it was, with some of the workers during a series of what he called "history lessons". He had said:

'World capitalism, and mass society, began their decline around 2008. The total profits that capitalism needed to survive were not restored after the economic downturn.'

'Why?' they'd asked. The young ones like Rosa not even entirely sure what mass society was.

'Because trade union struggles at the time were successful, and also because historically in times of crisis, capital undergoes financial expansion. But at that point in history it couldn't really financialise any more than it already was. Resources were becoming scarce. The unity of the world market was undermined when a bloc of countries led by China reneged on trade agreements, after that the United States refused to adjust to its diminished role in the global political economy. It clung to power and so the whole world-economy collapsed.'

'But what happened in this country?'

'In the UK, the policies of the Tory/Lib Dem coalition, then the Torys after the Conservative and Liberal Democrat parties merged, left millions unemployed and with virtually no welfare state left to rely on. Demand fell dramatically. Mass protest movements ensured a crisis of hegemony for all of the main political parties. Many of those that had the means to, emigrated where they could. Part of my family left for Australia.'

'Mine went back to Chile', Rosa said.

Philip nodded. 'In London especially, black markets flourished, in-kind trading became more and more important. With little money around, and as food imports ground to a standstill, the people who were left turned to small-scale agriculture to survive.'

In Philip's experience, London's shift in economies hadn't been easy. There were simply too few people around with the knowledge, skills, and capital to develop efficient farms, creating a highly exploitative situation for workers. He had had little choice but to take up work on one of the estates.

The government still existed, though the distinction between the government and the people had collapsed. Society was one big hierarchy, with the government at the top, then the Bosses. The workers like Ana, who didn't have inheritable leases to property, were at the bottom.

Philip opened the door just slightly and Rosa and Ana squeezed themselves inside, bent over double in the hope that they wouldn't be seen. Philip smiled.

'Hello Rosa, Ana. Welcome.'

He beckoned them into the front room, dimly lit with candles. Four other guards were already seated.

'You know Ricky, James, Dave, Anil.'

The rest of the guards greeted them softly as they sat down on the carpeted floor. Rosa noted the conspicuous absence of the guard who'd alerted the Boss to the strange men's presence.

'Of course you know that you've put us all at some risk by coming here. Surely you're bored by now of my stories. Can I guess? You want to know who the men who came again today were, what they said.'

'Yes, yes we do,' Rosa replied. 'They made him very angry.'

Philip eyed them cautiously. 'So you are simply curious?' he asked.

Rosa and Ana nodded.

'Well,' Philip cleared his throat. 'They are from a fringe political party reminiscent of the parties of old. This party is called the Real Communist Party of Britain – Seventh International (RCPB-7I). They wanted all of the workers here to join what they call the Official Workers Resistance to the New Feudalism. In truth some of the workers', he pointed at Dave, 'for instance, Dave I hope you don't mind, are already party members. The party has an internet presence, some information-sharing and communication is happening. Their strategy and tactics though are as yet ill-defined. But, of course, many other workers, like Neil of our team who informed the Boss of the men's presence, know that we are being exploited in our situation, but fear an alternative that is even worse.'

Rosa said, 'I thought it would be something like this for the Boss to have become so angry. I've seen their website before.' Ana looked at Rosa, surprised that she had divulged this fact to Philip.

Philip now stared at Rosa with even more surprise showing on his face.

'You have?'

Rosa stopped herself from asking why that would surprise him.

Philip continued, 'Well actually the party members were most interested in talking to the workers like you – women, minority ethnic workers. They figure you lot won't yet have heard the party messages, won't have joined the resistance.' His tone betrayed that he thought this a reasonable conclusion for the party members to have reached.

'They will be back, in spite of the Boss and his guns.'

The following afternoon Rosa and Ana worked their own farm with their team-mates, Erika, Magdalena, and Silvia. Rosa turned her eyes away from the bright summer sun. She thought that she saw a figure edging along the inside perimeter of the tall estate fence towards them. As her eyes adjusted to the light she saw for certain that it was three people. Three men. She blew a whistle to signal her *compañeras* to join her near the small house.

'I think that it might be those strange men, coming here,' Rosa said.

Erika was worried. 'Will they get us into trouble with the Boss? Perhaps we should go inside.'

'We've not done anything wrong. Disappearing from the field would just arouse more suspicion', Ana reasoned.

The men approached, slightly out of breath, and looked about them. They were dressed in green coverall fatigues similar to the grey ones that the workers wore. Rosa stood at the head of the group of women. The man in front addressed her, holding out his hand.

'My name is Member #66995. We are from the Real Communist Party of Britain – Seventh International (RCPB-7I). We...'

'We know who you are', Rosa interrupted him, ignoring his hand.

'Do you?' the man was surprised. 'I suppose you must have heard it from some of the other workers, the guards perhaps, by now.'

'Please say what you have to say quickly and leave, so as not to put both us and yourselves at further risk,' Rosa said.

The man looked taken aback at having been addressed so brusquely, but after swallowing, began:

'We believe that the workers' interests are inherently at odds with those of the Bosses, and that united we are stronger. That together we can take over the farms, by force if necessary, and not only end our own exploitation by the Bosses, but create more efficient and productive farms, in the hands of elected workers committees. We know that this might sound scary to you all, but we need as many workers to join us as possible in order to succeed. Will you join the Official Workers Resistance to the New Feudalism? If it makes you feel more inclined to join, we can set up a Women's Committee, a Black and Minority Ethnic committee. We will be most effective if we are all united.'

The man stopped, opened and closed his mouth a couple of times, looking unsure that he'd said all he'd planned to say.

Rosa allowed a long pause before she replied, 'What makes yours the "official" resistance?' she asked.

'Well—' the man stopped. One of his comrades answered, 'Ours is the only communist party left today. Search for yourself and you will see that this is true.'

Rosa turned to look at her *compañeras* to see if they had anything to add. They looked as bemused as she felt.

'Thank you for coming today. We will take it under consideration. Now you should go.'

***

That night, before Lights Time, Rosa went to the computers in one of the Boss's buildings. There was no one else around. She looked again at the website of 'RCPB-7l'. There were reams of text describing the vision the man had outlined – more efficient farms run by elected workers committees. There were more recently added poor translations into Spanish, and she assumed as poor into Bengali, Polish, Yoruba. As Philip had said, there was little concrete information about their strategy and tactics, but Rosa thought that that was fair enough at this stage. What bothered her was the lack of any information that might actually be useful to workers, like information about work that was available. All the resources put into building this website and none of it helpful, she thought.

As Rosa walked back to her house she was alarmed to see the shape of someone running towards the workers houses, seemingly from the front gate. None of the workers would draw attention to themselves by running like that unless something was very wrong. She was relieved to get home and close her front door behind her. Before she had finished putting on the kettle there was a knock.

Rosa looked above her at the clock on the wall – 9:32pm.

Her *compañeras* had also heard the knock. They now joined her in the front room. Rosa opened the door to a thin young man dressed in black.

'Was that you who I saw running through the estate a few moments ago?' she asked in place of a greeting. The young man looked around behind him before answering. 'Yes, it was me. Can I come inside?'

Rosa let him into the entranceway for her own safety and that of her team-mates. Ana addressed the young man sharply, 'You shouldn't run through estates like that, it puts all of the workers who live in them everyday under suspicion after you leave. And it is past the Lights Time here. Where have you come from?'

'I am camped near the road with a few others from my organisation. It's very dangerous so we'll be moving on soon.'

'Why have you come here?'

'I am from an organisation that we'd like you and others you know to join. All of the workers know that this new feudal society we are living in is unfair for us', the young man stated, obviously. 'Some others would have you believe that the solution is to create even more levels of hierarchy, in the form of workers' committees.'

He continued, 'We believe that any form of hierarchical government is inherently aggressive. We think that what is needed is a return to the individualism of the times before – the individual is the most important unit in society, and no one, other individuals or governments, has the right to curtail his or her freedom. We can all live peacefully under the principle that no one will violate our freedom and we will not violate anyone else's. The farms should be controlled by all of the workers operating on this principle equally. We are asking that you join the Libertarian Anarchist Resistance Movement.'

Magda and the others looked sceptical.

'How many members do you have?'

'We cannot be sure. We have a website with more information about what we believe which many workers may have looked at.'

'Are they all like you?' The young man at first looked as if he didn't know what she meant, until he looked at each of the five women in turn. 'I only know some of the members. I cannot be sure.'

'Thank you for speaking with us but you're quite possibly violating our freedom on our estate and in our house,' Rosa said. 'Now you should go.'

In the following days on the estate, the workers spoke within their families and teams about little else but the visits of the men. No one knew for sure how many of the houses the men had managed to call on but it seemed they had both targeted the North West Quadrant, where the Boss had put the houses of the all-women teams and the black workers teams. He always assigned like with like – as he saw it.

The workers, even timid ones like Neil, couldn't help but feel buoyed by the knowledge that there were many opposed to the way that they lived. Amongst Rosa and Ana's team they discussed their impressions of the two organisations at length. They all saw little value in joining either. There were more immediate issues to deal with, on top of their long labouring hours.

When they were finished working for the day on the farm or in the Boss' kitchens, Rosa and Ana were busy at the computers, though they had to be careful when others were present in the computer rooms. They tried to get the little information that was around about jobs and houses made available to the workers who needed it, those for whom the situation had become so unbearable on their own estates that they had to leave.

One evening Rosa received an email with a particularly desperate subject line, which she saw after she'd decrypted the message using PGP: 'Please help, workers are trapped!' The message was from a worker on an estate in Southwark. In poor English, it stated that workers from that estate had attempted to leave, to try to find free land that they could farm for themselves. On that estate, it said, workers were locked into their houses every night. A worker had gone into labour, had been unable to get help.

She had died. It was her partner who tried to leave with other members of her family.

The workers who had escaped had been caught and were now being held prisoner, without food, in order to create an example for the whole estate. This is what would happen to any other workers who tried to leave, a message that Rosa and all who'd grown up on the estates knew well.

Rosa was startled when she got to the end of the message. It said that the sender had tried to contact both the Real Communist Party of Britain – Seventh International (RCPB-7I), and the Libertarian Anarchist Resistance Movement for help, and had received no reply.

Rosa took the risk of going where she had no business and walked to the front gate to speak to Dave of the guard team, the only RCPB-7I party member who she knew.

'Dave. I've received a message from Southwark asking for help. Workers are being held prisoner.'

Dave raised his eyebrows in surprise. 'Why did you receive this message?'

Rosa was impatient.

'There's no time for that. What I came to ask is this: the message said that the RCPB-7I had been contacted for help, and that no response was received. Do you know anything about that? Can the party do anything to mobilize its members to help? People need to go to that estate, or workers will die, and the rest will continue to be treated as subhuman.'

Dave cleared his throat.

'Well, as a matter of fact I and a couple of others are responsible for our email communications. We didn't see the message. As to mobilizing the members, they are spread around the country and we are not able to contact all of them. We could try to gather some that are based in south London, but I think that in order to be at all effective or successful we would need others too.'

Rosa was silent for a moment, thinking. 'Don't you encrypt your emails?' she asked finally. 'The request for help was sent with PGP.'

'Well... no we don't.'

Rosa sighed.

'I will try to gather others to help. I'll need a day. Let's plan to send a contingent to the estate on Saturday, in two days time.'

Rosa returned to the computers. She contacted the Libertarian Anarchist Resistance Movement herself, figuring that, like the RCPB-7I, they may not have received the PGP message. She asked them to gather as many as they could to assemble outside of the south London estate on Saturday, at 12pm.

Later Rosa talked the situation over with her teammates.

'Of course, even supposing the RCPB-7I and the Libertarian Anarchist Resistance Movement are able to turn people out on Saturday, the workers contingent is likely to have only basic weapons,' Ana offered. 'We have no way of knowing what weapons the Boss will have.'

'But if the estate is anything like this one, the Boss doesn't really need to have a lot of weapons. Isn't that the whole point of this system? During capitalism, a worker's exploitation was hidden insofar as it appeared they were paid for every working hour—'

Silvia finished Rosa's thought, 'Though of course not for the actual value of their work.'

'Precisely. However, we know exactly where our exploitation is centered. It's the third of the potato starch and vodka we give to the Boss every year, and the three days of the week that we work for him. We know how much of our labour is for ourselves, and how much is for him and the maintaining this structure. But exactly *because* we have control over much of our work and our time, and our own way of producing in the form of this farm, the complacency of most of the workers is assured and weapons are not required,' Rosa finished.

'But it sounds as though this estate is different,' Ana returned. 'The workers are locked into their houses every night. They can't therefore be very content.'

'And if the two organisations on board are only able to supply a few people, the only way that we will be successful is if the workers there are not content.'

They finished talking, all knowing that the question of weapons that could be used against them was unresolved; that going to the south London estate was a big risk.

Rosa and Ana spent the remainder of the evening contacting people, requesting them to attend on Saturday. Though members of no organisation, they were linked into local Hackney-based activist networks that were older than they were. Rosa and Ana didn't know the origin of the networks, but they knew they sprung from a tradition of multiracial organising in the borough. They had existed and strengthened at the time of the Poll Tax boycott, enabling word to spread that people would refuse to pay.

When global capitalism began its collapse, the networks were large, loose alliances of activists unaffiliated to political parties, who mobilized for common, and mainly anti-capitalist aims. They had successfully disrupted the Olympics in 2012 by blockading the media and broadcast centres in Hackney Wick so that journalists could not enter and the games couldn't be broadcast as planned. With all eyes on London, the police had been restrained.

The networks had no central communication or official membership. Each individual linked into another and passed information to their own pool of contacts who they trusted. Rosa contacted a woman called Marai, knowing that she in turn would contact others.

They waited.

***

Early on Saturday, before Lights Time ended at 5:30pm, Ana said goodbye to her teammates.

'I wish that we could come with you,' Erika said.

Rosa smiled. 'But the decision to send just one person from each family or team is sensible. This way people are less likely to be missed and those left are therefore less likely to be under suspicion.'

They wished Ana good luck.

Ana left to meet others at the gate. She walked softly, avoiding the floodlights. She heard movement behind her. She assumed that it would be another worker heading south.

She felt the pain before she could turn and register what was happening. She turned to meet the furious gaze of the Boss.

***

Rosa tired of waiting for Ana's return. After Lights Time she crept carefully to the house of the guards. She knocked softly on the door.

Philip's face was tired but happy.

'Rosa. Come in.' When she was safely inside he humbly congratulated her on organising the day's mission. 'You turned out an impressive number, and together with Dave and a handful of his RCPB – 7I comrades, and a few of those anarchists, we were successful. After the guards let us into the estate with virtually no protest, the vast majority of the workers of the estate stopped what they were doing to join us and entered the Boss's main building. We demanded the release of those who were being held prisoner, and the improvement of conditions on the estate. The Boss was utterly overwhelmed by our presence and acquiesced quickly. I hope that our actions today will have brought hope to all of the estates.'

Rosa was surprised at Philip's praise.

'Where is Ana?' she asked. 'She's not come back to the house.'

Philip's face seemed to grey slightly as he opened his mouth to reply. He paused.

'But she never turned up this morning at the gate.'

They each realised what must have happened. It would have been, Rosa knew, the third time that Ana had been caught out after Lights Time since she'd arrived on the estate.

Rosa had grown up in the estates where individual people, who came and went, were accorded far less importance than in the past. She thought briefly of all the others who may have been caught heading south that morning, or who may have been punished when they returned home. She was pleased that the prisoners had been freed, allowed to return to their houses and to work.

Rosa said goodbye to Philip and walked home.

# IV

Clapton

# Demolition: Clapton Park Estate 1993

*By Kieran Duddy*

'Look, it isn't working,' my girlfriend said. 'I am sorry but that is all I have to say.'

Just then the explosion at the base of the buildings fractured every beam in the block. Cracks shot through the concrete. Deep wounds opened up, exposing the living quarters of generations of families.

Bedrooms, bathrooms and stairways were ripped and twisted. Like a wounded giant, the towers shuddered, became limp then folded in on themselves and hit the ground with one almighty crash.

The crowd stared in silence while the boiling dust rose from the rubble and climbed towards the sky. The sun disappeared.

I stared at Jane whose face was woven with terror.

'What is that?' She asked.

We looked back.

An enormous cloud of dust was rolling in the direction of the crowd. The stillness broke. Panic swept through the throngs of people. There were curses and screams. Children were pulled off their feet. Men and women began running from the cloud unfurling above us like a dark veil. I looked for Jane. I called her name.

Further along the marshes I saw her tiny sprinting figure disappearing into the distance. On my left people battled to gain access to the marquee, while outside dozens removed items of clothing in a useless attempt to protect their faces from the dust. My eyes began to sting. The last thing I saw was bodies curling up into balls on the ground. I began to choke. I joined my fallen comrades on the grass.

I waited to die.

A man's voice woke me from my nightmare. 'Jeeeesus, that was something else.'

I opened my eyes and stared at the sky. Sunlight beat down on my face. I got off the ground.

People were standing around like zombies – coated from head to toe in dust.

'You got a light?' The man said. He stood beside me, patting his arms and legs.

We looked at each other.

People were walking along the marshes, an undiscovered planet now, completely drowned in dust.

'That was unbelievable,' the man said bursting into laughter.

I joined him, uncontrollably.

I would never see Jane again and in that moment it didn't really matter.

# A Hackney Triptych

*By David Dawkins*

## Lower Clapton Road

Traffic moves in eight directions along the road outside the bookshop. Life seems to move at different speeds for different people – car to bike to pedestrian and back again. The school children picking at cardboard tubs of chicken 'n chips – walking, talking – listening to tin-pop hip-hop from their mobile phones. They follow the thread trail of pigeon-picked chicken bones, the marrow tips moving them through the territory around the familiar haunts, kicking litter, playing, making fun of the Polish, and the Polish looking sour and grumbling back. Their booze-reddened, weather-worn faces following their own thread: that of people, friends, other Hackney street folk, the trail of squashed Special Brew tins from bus-stop-station to the mattress stash, their tarpaulin shelter behind St. John's. Zooming past the slowly trudging Polish men, the young, plaid-shirted-bed-haired cyclists en route to media jobs along Old Street, Shoreditch, Clerkenwell or Farringdon. They swerve between the potholes and tarmac lumps listening to the latest thing on the latest thing – iPods and big bucket headphones. Others listen to London. The 24/7 bin men, the hardest working men in Hackney, their flashing orange lights hitting the walls through the windows above, stopping to collect the huge canisters of vegetable oil from one house, cracked canvases and last year's Ikea furniture from the next – clogging up the bus lanes with banter – they calcify the city's capillaries, slowing the flow of people through the borough.

Inside the bookshop on Lower Clapton road, the manager opens the door to the storeroom and slaps the wall with a banana. Unable to locate the light switch with his wall-wandering banana-holding hand, and unable to put down the box of books weighing heavily on his other arm, he chooses to walk straight into the darkness and let the door close behind him.

His eyes adjust to the light and eventually the skyscraper outlines of stored books begin to distinguish themselves. Finding a space on the floor, the bookshop manager lets the box slide down his leg to the ground. Feeling content and comfortable in his surroundings, he peels, chomps and chews, slowly finishing his banana in the dark before trudging wearily upstairs and opening the shop for the day's trade.

*** 

A few hours pass before the bookshop manager, the man who had committed the acts of deviancy to women around Lower Clapton road, takes a huge swig of his tea and turns the page of his book. The phone rings.

'Hello, Pages of Hackney,' the man grumbles down the phone.

'Can I speak to David please?'

There is a long pause as the man collects himself. 'Mother. This is David.'

He sighs.

'Oh, I wasn't sure if it would be you who answered.'

'Mother, I am the only person who works here during the week. If you call during the week, it will always be me who answers.'

'That's good to know darling. How are you?'

'Fine.'

'How are you, in yourself?'

'Extra fine.'

'Really?'

'Yes mother.'

There is another long pause. It annoys David that his mother is probably grinning on the other end of the phone. He imagines his mother's old and simple face being cheerful, pleased to hear his voice – smiling.

'What did you have for dinner last night?' She asks.

In reality David had microwave chicken korma from Somerfield. He'd like to tell his mother that he had seven pints of lager and a bowl full of vaginas, but he resists and offers something a tad more likely.

'I had a Greek salad mother. I eat Greek salad quite often actually,' he states.

'Oh that sounds nice. What's in that then?'

'Tomatoes, cucumber, feta cheese, olives, olive oil, balsamic vinegar and garlic.'

'Oh, that sounds special. Olive oil! My word, you are getting good aren't you?'

'Yes.'

'We just had leftovers. Some leftover casserole from Sunday and stew from Monday. It was lovely. Your father had a yogurt for pudding. Peach, I think.' She speaks slowly, vowel sounds become days and commas feel like what it is to draw a curtain during daylight hours. But, there is buoyancy in her voice and he imagines a tiny Irishman sitting on her shoulder, kicking his jolly little heels against her and whistling a cheerful tune through a penny whistle.

David hates these subtle intonations of mild optimism. Stew and casserole are meals firmly embedded in the gastronomic armory of a person who views the world while drinking a glass half-empty. Stew and casserole are not reasons to be cheerful.

'Sounds nice.' He huffs.

'I read that book you gave me!'

'Oh yeah, which one?' David grunts. His mother being the main purchaser of every dog-eared and damaged book on the bookshop's shelves, one week she'll read *A History of London's Church Windows*, the next she'll read something by some French chap whose first name is Alain – French for Alan – and whose second name sounds like a piece of ornate cooking apparatus, Robbe-Grillet.

All returned books receive positive reviews.

'It was called, *The Girl with the Dragon Hat* by Steve Larsson.'

'*The Girl with the Dragon Tattoo* by Steig Larsson.' David corrects his mother.

'Oh yes. You're right, that's the one.'

'What did you think mother?'

'Well yes. I enjoyed it. Although it was very violent. It was good. Very thrilling, but very violent, especially towards women.'

'Sorry, did that bother you?' David asks.

'Oh no, not at all. Thank you for lending it to me.'

\*\*\*

A few hours later David stands in the aisles of Palm 2 Super Market studying the various flavors of Big Soup arranged on the shelves.

Palm 2, a strange little corner shop run by staff who – if they could – would bake, pasteurize, pickle, pick or grow each and every product for you should it not be on their shelves at the time of asking.

The place is something of a hotspot for the type of women that David hopes to one day meet and marry. In comparison to the horrid new shop-in-a-box Tesco that had just popped up along Lower Clapton Road that always seemed to have a packet of Danish bacon amongst the CDs and DVDs, and a dusty lettuce lurking menacingly in the darkest corner, Palm 2 is a haven for those who like to bask in the privilege of choice.

Deciding on the Sausage and Vegetable variety of Big Soup, David tosses the tin in his hand like a cricket ball, only to drop it and have it land on his polished brogue and roll along the spice aisle. With a bowed back, scampering with short steps, arms extended, he follows the soup along the floor. The soup stops at a pair of pristine white pumps.

'What are you doing in here?'

David's head rises up and along a long pair of thin legs, over the hem of a short floral dress and into the eyes of an unimpressed-looking woman. Lucy Pith-Smythe momentarily turns away, only to pick up a packet of tagliatelle, check for undesirable additives, and drop the pasta into the basket with a soft splash of its plastic packet. Just back from a run, she is freshly showered and glowing.

'Just picking up some soup.'

'I can see that.'

The bookshop manager stands. He shows her the Big Soup,

holding it in front of her and hoping that she'd be impressed by the fact that it contains vegetables. Lucy is an inch taller than David whose back and shoulders have long since buckled under the severe weight of carrying such a large burden of cynicism for such a long period of time. Although she is older, Lucy looks a lot younger than David; her hair shines, whereas the hair on David's head is dusty and wiry – in fact identical in texture and colour to that inside his armpit and on the underside of his scrotum. She has thick pink lips that always seem to have that freshly bitten flush of colour. David's lips are thin. The last days of a flaking, yellow cold sore crumble into his pepper-patch stubble of his beard. There is a long history that precedes this chance meeting.

'Can I just ask, why did you say that I look like Linda Hamilton from *Terminator 2*?' Lucy snaps. 'Were you trying to be funny?' She puts a hand on the curve between her breast and hip.

David has to think about this for a while. He thinks about pulling down her knickers and hiding under her skirt and breathing deeply. He looks at the ingredients written on the green tin of his Big Soup, and then back to Lucy, then back to the ingredients, then back to Lucy. Her glare remains steadfast and significantly more penetrative than he could claim to have been during the last two years.

'I thought it was a compliment?'

They look at each other for a long moment.

'No. Just... no. It isn't a compliment.'

And with that she walks away.

## The Round Chapel

Billy fucking Bragg played here last year. I can't remember where I was last year. But I definitely wasn't here watching Billy fucking Bragg.

SALSA CLASSES EVERY WEDNESDAY 8PM – ALL LEVELS WELCOME. The sign in the background billows in the breeze as I slip under the police tape and nod to the officers first on the scene.

I went dancing once. I went dancing once with my wife, my ex-wife. I can remember going, I can remember my wife, but I can't remember the dancing.

According to the report I'd half listened to down at the station:

At approximately 12:30pm, Monica Delaney, a housewife and former chartered accountant on maternity leave, left her house on Clapton passage and crossed the road at the zebra crossing. She walked past Harris Electrical, past Powerscroft Road and continued on this route past the Round Chapel until she turned left at the second-hand furniture shop, down Glenarm Road. In the shadow of the Round Chapel, it happened again. Monica Delaney was en route to Chatsworth Road to meet a friend at Venetia's Café for a coffee when she was attacked.

When I arrive at the scene the victim has been wrapped in a metallic blanket and is being dutifully attended to by the emergency services. The sky that had probably been blue when she had set off has greyed, and a slow drizzle pats the canopy of leaves above the steps of the chapel. It is fucking cold and the wind sweeps empty beer cans and crisp packets across the floor as police radios crackle and chime with words and information that everyone just seems to ignore, as if there is some other language to this place just floating around in the air, waiting for children to burst like rainbow-tinted bubbles in the air.

It is noisy, yet no one is talking. Crowds of locals encircle the cordoned area. I see the local winos try to explain what happened by pointing and shouting, then asking for money. Old Hackney women of every ethnic denomination stop, look for a moment, then shake their heads and slowly walk away dragging their shopping in two-wheeled tartan trolleys along the uneven cobblestones. Other people – black, white, asian – shake hands and hug, just using this bizarre moment as a reason to get together and remember things that have happened in their sad little lives.

Community Officer Okoah is the first to approach me.

'Everything is the same.' He states shaking his head and pulling his wrists from the luminous fabric of his long sleeves, his radio chirping and crackling.

'How so?' I reply at the end of my breath, at the end of my tether.

'The victim is a woman.' Okoah, a forty-seven-year-old former lollipop man is worth everything and nothing.

'Okoah, you deserve every penny of that unpaid wage.'

'Thank you, Sir.'

Monica Delaney's face is obscured between the plastic oxygen mask and her long blonde fringe. She raises her head a little to look at me. The boys were right; she is what forensics might call (dead or alive) a damn fine specimen. The kind of woman I see around these parts all the time. I need answers. I stand by her. I stand over her.

She looks up at me from below, her black lashes wet with tears as if she'd just finished choking on something she couldn't swallow.

The oxygen cracks through her lips like a whistle of wind through a barn door. There's a wedding ring on her finger and a mobile phone lit up in her hand – but that's all. Two sad little symbols of hope, of a connection to something that isn't really here. I stare at her for a few more moments than I would otherwise be allowed.

The beige-faced paramedic, cleaning the gravel from her grazed knee with a jam jar of antiseptic and a cotton bud, turns to me and shakes his head. She isn't ready for me yet. As I step away I hear her sobbing against the oxygen mask and the paramedic having to help her breath. I don't turn around.

I take a turn around the back of the chapel to retrace where the assailant may have been hiding, or where he might have come from. As the echo of the flashing lights fades, I find myself somewhere very different. From the front, the Round Chapel is a handsome building, new without being modern, old without being a fucking ruin. A bit like me.

I step into the large shadow that the chapel casts behind itself. The floor is made of damp mud, dog excrement and weather-faded crisp packets. I tread carefully, only stopping to pick up a few cigarette butts and zip them into a plastic bag. I sniff them all. They've been smoked in the last few hours. All of them are warm and dry.

No one has since passed and trod them into the ground. I pull out a cigarette of my own. I smoke the same brand. I lean down and touch the mud. My footprints are the same size, same shoe – flat and leather soled brogues – as these footprints. The assailant must have come from the other direction. He must have stood here and watched her.

In the darkest nook, up against the chapel wall, where the rainwater runs off the roof and turns the sandstone green, a little swamp of used condoms sits in a puddle like bird shit beneath a lamppost. I put on my gloves and pick them all up one by one, pinching the entrance closed. A trickle of moisture runs up my sleeve into the nook of my forearm. Muddy-water, blood, lubricant and semen drip from the tweezers on the pile making a sound that reminds me of raindrops on the roof of my tent, my home.

Through the leaves, out from the back of the chapel, I can see the windows and door to my ex-wife's house. She lives there with my daughter and another man, a new man. We don't speak much. We don't speak ever. She left me years ago.

I approach their house and move around their car, accidentally walking right through the row of flowers on their drive. I snap the ankles of a tulip. The flower flops to the ground with a soft thud of its red face.

They have a car, a new Volvo parked outside. I look through the windows and see my daughter's toys across the back seat. Her favourite book – *The Little Prince* – tucked into the back of the seat in front of the booster seat, an empty Happy Meal box on the floor beneath.

'Can I help you Robert?' I could recognise the sharp hi-de-fucking-hi intonation of my ex-wife from a mile away. As a child I used to eat whole sticks of chalk. My ex-wife's voice has the same effect on my ears as the chalk had on my mouth.

'Nice car. What is it? Diesel? 1.4? 1.6? four-by-four? Nice.'

'It's Alain's. He's had it for a while now.'

'You're with a fucking French guy?'

'What are you doing here Robert?'

With my hands on my hips I turn slowly in a circle, looking at the floor, nodding and breathing angrily through my nose. I'd seen someone do something similar in a cop show once and I'd always thought that it looked pretty fucking intense. I'd also seem them solve crimes.

Walking along the pavement in a world of his own, a sad looking father with a salt-and-pepper side parting and wearing a waxed Barbour jacket with a natty purple scarf walks through the middle of us, holding a child's scooter by its ankles and in deep conversation with the pavement in front of his feet. We both look away. My ex-wife shakes her head as if expecting some sort of answer.

'There's been another incident. Another woman has just been assaulted, just behind the Round Chapel. I just came round to tell you to be careful.'

'What happened?' she asks.

'Same as last time. Same as the Clapton Passage assaults, but this time he's a little further out. He's getting more confident. This isn't the last time he'll strike. This is probably just the beginning.'

This shocks her.

'What do you mean, "the same"?'

'The victim is a white upper-middle-class female, in her late 20s to early-30s, attractive, confident, strong. She was attacked in daylight, in a public area, from behind —'

'Then what?'

'Well — Are you sure?'

'Yes, Robert.'

She thinks I'm patronising her. She doesn't like it.

'Ok, well according to reports, the assailant approached from behind and proceeded to unbuckle her belt and then unbutton the victim's jeans. Without struggle or resistance, he then pulled down the jeans and undergarments of the victim, paused for a second doing something that we do not know, and walked away. Same method – same result. The victim breaks down and is rescued ten to fifteen minutes later when someone sees her crying, standing bolt upright, not having moved an inch. As soon as they are touched, they fall to the floor and curl up like an acorn, crying and fitting. You know how it works.'

My ex-wife places the flat of her hand against her chest. She is afraid, and in a way I am happy.

She rocks for a moment and I see a corridor of toys scattered across the floor behind her legs. I see a toy truck, a blonde doll, there are six little crayon marks on the doorframe behind, each one representing the height of my daughter during the years that have passed since I last saw her little face. I see three sets of Wellington boots in a row. Two pairs are green, one pair is smaller, greener and has the faces of little frogs on the toes.

I don't deserve this, I don't deserve this life – beautiful wife, happy child, nice house on Powerscroft Road, a fucking Volvo, Billy fucking Bragg – these are not things I know much about. I feel a burning desire to return to the condoms and spunk behind the Round Chapel.

'Listen, I've got to go.' I wave while turning.

'Robert,' she calls to me.

I turn.

'Good luck,' she says. I don't hear the door close. I like to think that she's watching me while I walk away.

## Hackney Downs

The fat man breathes heavily and stretches his groin.

'Ah, here she is. Hi Luce,' Tom says, red in the face, standing in a lunge position, his grinning marionette facial features as shiny as his bare sweaty neck and his blue shell suit. Woodlice scatter, he shuffles his feet leaving two huge indents in the soft grass as if a tent had been pitched there the night before.

Lucy, dressed in a vest displaying all the barbed musculature of Linda Hamilton from the hit movie, *Terminator 2*, slowly raises the flat of her hand and waves at her two "friends".

'Hi Lucy.' Little Janet Pickering wriggles her fingertips. Lucy nods and returns the wave with something more like the crumpled face of a flatulent baby than a genuine smile.

'Do you need to stretch?' Bowles asks.

'No. Let's just go.'

The three of them set off around the park at a leisurely pace, the dogs follow in a single whirlwind of fighting, fucking and running like Tasmanian Devils behind. No one talks.

Tom Bowles, the chief organiser of this run, is fat like an onion bulb in a chicken's arse and, as such, has all the mannerisms of a huffing, puffing, burping, staggering fat man when it comes to jogging. When he's out, either at the gym or for a run, Tom will talk about nothing but exercise. When he's at home he does nothing but buy, prepare, cook and eat food. As if warming his hands by the red embers of a fire, he is comforted by the glow of his computer screen and will stay up long into the night looking through the various shopping baskets aligned as tabs on his Internet browser, juggling his generous budget to get as much gourmet food from the various supermarkets and organic produce suppliers that deliver in the area. Long stalks of organic asparagus, king shrimps like legs of chicken, olives as large as greasy apples, Bowles has expensive tastes and, despite the running – an ever expanding waistline.

'So what's new with you, Luce?'

'Nothing much.'

'How's Adam? Where's he watching the game on Sunday?'

'Fine. Yep, still fine.'


Lucy, a friend of Tom's through her husband's connections, is someone who walks barefoot over the bleeding edge of Hackney life. She is married to a man she loves but hardly knows. A former male model, now a "Creative Director" of a large corporate strategy and graphic design agency on Old Street, he is – all things considered – a loving man and a good husband. Lucy used to be an architect, now she's a wife who spends her days either waiting for her husband to bring his penis home, or plucking carrots at her allotment. Sometimes she walks around Hackney buying popular Scandinavian crime novels from the local bookshop, drinking coffee at the various coffee shops or plotting feckless sexual affairs with the dapper, dead-eyed and cheekbone-cheerful young boys she often meets in vintage shops a little further afield. All things considered, she thinks of her life as like an all-you-can-eat vegan buffet – there's a lot of food on her plate but obviously a few crucial ingredients missing from her meal.

'How did little Danny get on at that after-school art class?' Bowles now leans to the right and asks Janet.

'Yeah, fine.'

'When's the private view?'

Janet pretends to laugh, 'Well he's already better than most of the new lot round here. We're aiming to go straight to the White

Cube, bypass the riff-raff.' They snigger at the lucklessness of the generation below.

Lucy's supposed "friend" and running partner, Janet Pickering, is someone who goes for a run wearing baggy beige pajama bottoms and a baby blue fleece. Her sleeves flap as her knees buckle with each gravel-scratch of her scampering feet. While running, her face is like that of someone whose inner thighs were being tickled by an elephant's trunk from behind, always dashing, always red-eyed, always twitching from left to right, hyper-aware, always smiling – teeth first, shoulders last.

'We haven't had an incident for a while now have we?' Bowles breaks the silence with the kind of question that could only ever warrant more silence. He nods to himself when neither of them replies. 'I wonder if they caught him?' Still nothing but heavy breathing and raised eyebrows. All he wants is for one of them to say something sexual, anything, to make the day worth living. Even the word "hard" would do. A bead of sweat drips from his nose. His face – red and drenched – is made further ridiculous by his stone-dry Hasselhoff hair-do.

'He's probably moved on,' he adds, 'they're saying that it's all about Peckham, New Cross, Deptford these days. You know, south of the River.'

While the dogs Martin Amis (a Yorkshire Terrier), John Snow (a Boston Terrier), Brian Blessed (a flabby grey Neapolitan Mastiff) and Tea Cup (a sand-coloured and slender-hipped Whippet) dart, bark, rumble, fucking one another silly in the periphery of their masters' vision, Bowles, the owner of Martin Amis, the least fuckable of all the dogs, looks from left to right wanting to talk. The run continues in silence. All three of them envy the dogs.

They stop for a stretch. Bowles looks at the two women and has a good old think to himself. He thinks about Janet Pickering, with her tiny eyes like a blackbird and her blue veins like roads on an A to Z map beneath her translucent, tracing-paper thin skin. Every morning, Bowles masturbates in the shower. It is not difficult to imagine what he thinks about whilst leaning up against the shower wall, squinting, moaning, his fat hand wiping away the beads of water and the condensation inside his cubicle as he tugs away.

Still stretching and watching the two women, Bowles imagines lifting that baggy blue fleece over her glockenspiel ribs and porcelain tits. He imagines smiling, calmly, knowingly at her docile face as it came out from under the fabric and running the flat of his large palms down the notches and lumps of her glacial body. Bowles often likes to imagine that, for a man like himself, seducing Janet Pickering might almost be easy...

... They would sit side-by-side sipping wine and eating olives in the candle light of her austere redbrick home. The odd toy – a truck, a naked Barbie, a Crayola crayon – would pepper the floor of her stay-away husband's expensive apartment, doing little to disrupt the skeletal symmetry along the lines of the beech veneer floor and the strong, white roof beams of her modern home.

They would laugh, touch hands and talk of food, of children and other neighbours along the Clapton Passage. She would laugh at his jokes and not interrupt when he stated things as fact that she knew were not strictly true.

When the moment was right, he'd stand and pull her up from the armpits until she was vertical, holding her like a child with one hand beneath her pit, tracing his fingers slowly down her thin neck and along the prominent ledge of her collarbone.

To a soundtrack of something minimal, something classical – Phillip Glass or Michael Nyman perhaps – Bowles would then place the entirety of his fat hand over her chest and scrunch the fabric of her floral blouse into itself. She'd melt. He'd flip her around until she was in front of him facing the same way. As if operating a piece of machinery, he'd break her posture at the waist leaning forwards like an animal as he stood over her, pulling the hair at its root down the nape of her neck. A fox would cross the garden and trip the spot light. It would stop and watch, its huge pupils black and glowing like polished 8-balls. The fox, cocking its head to one side, would see on the other side of the glass conservatory, little Janet Pickering, flattening her left hand and her right forearm against the glass as the top of her head rhythmically bumped, and the condensation of her breath bloomed and retreated like the first patches of ice clouding a pool of water with each quickening breath. Tucking each one of his fingers between the taught rack of ribs along her back and running his thumbs down her spinal column, Bowles imagines the dry slap of his testicles on her hard, white, body and the steady thud of her head banging harder and harder against the glass. Eventually he would punch her, punch her very, very hard in the back of the head. Then, in that quiet and still moment as she was still thinking about what had just happened and reaching upwards to touch the nape of her head for blood, he'd do it again and again and again, and again. Then he'd ejaculate inside her, finishing his wine with a swig and smacking his lips –

Ahhhhhhhhhhhhhhhhhhhhhhhhhhhhhhhhhhhhhhhhhhhhhhhhhhh.

1995 – a good year, he might say to himself while looking into the glass and rolling it between his fingers with a slow and gentle twitch of his wrist.

As little Janet Pickering wobbled around on her feet, her face bumping and smudging into the glass as if drunk or dizzy, Bowles imagines standing up still inside her and telling her about the tyre pressure on his Volvo and a long-distance business trip to Milton Keynes he had planned for the following Tuesday. He imagines moving a bowl of olives from a side-table onto the flat of her back and then tossing them into his mouth by the handful, slowly chewing but letting the pips dribble from his lips and pitter-patter down over her shoulders and onto the floor. Eventually, he'd leave the room and she'd fall over, gathering herself inwards like an acorn. After a few minutes he'd reappear, in nothing but his socks, shirt and tie, his leg hairs erect like the bristles of a toilet brush. He'd smile as little Janet Pickering rose to her feet and tied a Windsor knot around his neck, pulling the knot tight and sealing the moment with a kiss...

'Are you finished Tom?' Lucy Pith-Smythe asks, noticing him daydreaming and staring at Janet Pickering as she bent down and stretched her hamstrings in front of him.

'Yes, yes. Quite. Just thinking about dinner.'

# Electric Blue

*By Ania Ostrowska*

The bike leaning nonchalantly against the shop window was a sleek vintage road Peugeot with an elegant blue frame and thin, worn-down tyres with show-off blue rims. She knew this bike. She used to know this bike intimately. Back then, though, its saddle was white, not stupidly out-of-place mauve.

He would never get a saddle like that, she thought. She took another sip of Turkish coffee, courtesy of Palm 2 in Clapton Pond. It was too sweet, but she superstitiously followed the once received advice that strong coffee should be sweet to enhance its qualities.

She needed something strong to get out of the stupor she had found herself in. Life had been lazy recently, just like this peaceful summer evening by the Pond. Traffic wasn't too bad and she could hear stray gulls competing for a wavelength with overexcited local kids.

Breaking this almost rural idyll was a lit up Tesco Express sign to her left.

The fancy bike was bringing back unwanted memories

anyway. She might as well admit to herself that, yes, it was the Tesco they'd fought hand in hand to prevent from coming into being. Endless sessions at the Hackney Town Hall, half falling asleep while the councillors slowly made their way through endless complaints about some new developer's blocks of flats around Old Street, just to cheer or boo when they finally reached the last item on the agenda: a proposed new Tesco Express shop in Clapton Pond. All pertinent evidence had been heard, a procession of witnesses had paraded before the judges: the conservationist (it turned out that the Pond was a conservation area), the mother of young children crossing the road every day on their way to school, the Palm 2 employee afraid of losing her job and hence the support for her family. All this obstructed the application process. She smiled with satisfaction allowing sweet liquid to impregnate her tongue as she remembered young ambitious Tesco lawyers losing their professional cool over the line of local residents giving their testimony.

She came late to the first of these meetings and so ended up sitting next to him. He was at first aloof, pretending to be irritated by having to let go of his iPod. At meeting number three they were holding hands under the Town Hall's desks. He fingered diagrams showing in great detail the proposed loading bay while she dreamt of other fingerings that indeed followed in due course.

A sudden screech of brakes cut into her daydreaming. She moved her eyes from the bike to witness a cyclist performing a neck-breaking manoeuvre to avoid a huge delivery lorry parking in the loading bay. The guy nearly fell off his bike, swore heartily and pedalled away towards Hackney Baths. She sighed and rolled her eyes. No matter how obvious it had been that a loading bay in that spot would disrupt the traffic and make cyclists' lives even more miserable, for some reason the council accepted all the tortuous explanations delivered by smug boys in snug suits. As if the story had already been written, she thought bitterly.

Back to the bike in front of her. It couldn't possibly be his. After an outbreak of love between him and Alicia-The-Posh-Hippie, an outbreak of such unexpectedness and intensity paralleled only by a similar event that took place between the two of them just months earlier, when they moved out of E5 to some absurd location. Willesden Green? Holland Park? Within her frame of reference it might as well be Zurich. He surely wouldn't come round for a Turkish pizza or a chat with a friendly proprietor.

On the other hand, the Electric Blue Velocity rims... They were difficult to get hold of in this country, and quite expensive. Saving money on virtually everything, he splurged on his bicycle. Poser. The very last sip of coffee completed the lengthy process of waking her up just in time to stare, on a caffeine high, at the owner of the bike who had left the shop with bags full of groceries. A tall girl gave her a friendly look, slightly puzzled by the force of her stare. Her eyes were green.

# Hackney Numbers

*By Sam Berkson*

**I.**

At the end of the weekend
the neighbour's party shook the back wall
from their back garden where
a corner of theirs touches a corner of ours.
Banging house music
crashed into our house
giving our evening meal
a whole different ambience.

Who's to complain?
Sunday evening, still light and warm,
party with the kids, few beers and some tunes,
they're doing the right thing, right?
Besides, they've only recently moved in
been quiet till now
seem a nice family
but our tolerance becomes easier
when they put some old ska on.

## II.

Earlier that week,
the day after your screams
had pulled apart the night
and brought us to our windows,
the police sealed the mouths of the alley
with tape and stood watch,
closing the case.

Will they make one for you?
Else the humiliations of the night
stained orange in the streetlight
will play out in medical room,
police station and witness box,
repeating and petering out
to a sordid termination.

### III.

A little further south-east
where the crowded council estates meet
the busy deli counters,
where the drinkers on the street
aren't just the street drinkers;
the war across the divide breaks out:
primary school kids with water balloons
and a man with a camera takes a picture.

Captured on film:
tough little oiks
taunting water-splashed trendies...
And BANG!
He gets one in the lens too.

# V

Hackney Central

# The Finest Store

*By Kit Caless*

Craig opened the fridge door.

'Good morning, Craig. You have run out of milk,' the fridge said.

'Thanks Fridge, I already knew that,' he replied.

'You have run out of Finest Cheddar Cheese, Finest Toastie Loaf and Fantastic Mr Fudge too.'

'Thanks, anything else?'

'There is nothing else on your essentials list that you are running low on.'

'What about on my naughty list?'

'On your naughty list you are running low on McTaito's Oven Chips, Zoopy Milkshake and Kreme de la Kreme doughnuts. You are totally out of Bedazzles.'

'Hmm. Okay thanks.'

'No problem, Craig. Have a nice morning.'

The fridge printed out Craig's shopping list.

At the front door Craig scanned in his handcode. The door opened.

'Good Morning, Craig. Have a nice day,' said a sultry female voice over his P.A.

Craig smiled, 'Have a nice day too,' he said.

'Thanks, Craig,' the voice said in reply.

Craig glanced up at the ceiling and carried on out of the door.

'Don't forget, we've got a special offer on Finest Canadian Bacon, Finest New Zealand Chicken Eggs and Über-Finest Baked Beans from the Rhine,' the voice shouted after him.

Craig had forgotten, in fact he wasn't sure if he knew before, but regardless – thoughts of cereal disappeared, suddenly replaced by the prospect of a good English fry-up. He skipped towards the lift.

As the lift dropped fifteen floors, Craig went through his work schedule for the day. In front of the lift mirror he practised his stern face, his thank you face, his disappointed face and his that's-not-quite-what-I-had-in-mind face.

'Your face looks excellent today, Mr Brewster,' said the lift just before opening its doors at ground level.

'Ah, thanks Lift. The Finest Moisturiser you recommended has done wonders.'

'No problem, Craig. Every tiny bit helps.'

Once in the Shopping Arena, Craig made a beeline for the Breakfast Aisle on the Finest Side of the Arena. There he found his suggested items already put together and in a bag marked 'Craig Brewster'. Inside were Finest Eggs, Finest Bacon and the Finest Baked Beans. They had also thrown in some Super Dooper Fresh Pumped Orange Juice (oranges from Brazil flown over to Spain to be pumped with special Spanish hands), some Finest Milk and a Finest Toastie Loaf for good measure. Craig was pleased with what they had chosen; he wanted exactly what they had chosen.

Even though he didn't want any of it earlier.

Craig got on the travelator towards the check-out. As he glided along, enjoying the weight of his bag pulling on his arm, he looked across the Arena to the Value Side. He felt sorry for the Value People. Their Value Flats were basic to the point of offensive – at least, from what he saw on Finest TV. The bathrooms were fitted with a metal toilet bowl that had no seat, a shower that only gave out cold water and a sink made of plastic. The bedroom was also the kitchen, which was also the living room. Craig had an en suite bathroom but the Value Flat was en suite everything. There was one window in the whole flat and that was only opened once you'd collected enough StoreCard points.

Through the one-way mirror that divided them, he could just about make out one woman in ill-fitting blue and white Value Pyjamas. She was walking down the Breakfast Aisle just like he was a minute ago. She picked up her designated bag and pulled out each item at a time:

Value Kippers – half a kipper, unsmoked.

Value Freeze Dried Coffee – Not soluble.

Value Bread – Untoastable

Value Beans – Bake yourself.

Why would you be a Value Person? What would be in it for you?

Surely they couldn't just accept poor quality goods just because they cost less? Somehow the Value People didn't seem to know what they were consuming. Or at least they didn't know what else they could be consuming.

However, they seemed to be content. They smiled and chatted to each other, they walked happily towards the check out sniffing their odourless food as if it smelt like Finest Roses.

'Look around you!' Craig wanted to shout at them through the glass. 'Look at the plain colours and the tasteless food! What are you doing? Even the packaging is plain.'

But he knew they wouldn't hear him. The mirror was one way to stop the Value Folk from jealously coveting everything in the Finest Side. The mirror was soundproofed, placed there to stop the Finest People from having to hear the Value People's parsimonious conversations. All that talk of closed windows and canned peaches would be enough to make the Finest Person feel queasy.

When he reached the check-out, Craig smiled at the screen.

'Good morning, Craig Brewster. Do you have everything you want?'

The pretty girl on the screen had a very happy voice.

'How about a Snickers bar for the walk to your meeting?' she asked.

'A Snickers would be a good idea but—'

Craig didn't get a chance to finish his sentence with, 'I'm trying to lose weight,' before a king-size Snickers popped out from behind the screen and landed in his bag. Craig was so impressed with the aim of whatever was throwing the Snickers that he forgot he didn't actually want it. He thanked the screen and passed his handcode over the scanner. He walked back to the lift via the Garden Route.

After a sumptuous breakfast, Craig changed into his Finest Work Suit and took the Outside Lift down to Morning Lane. He ate his Snickers as he crossed over Mare Street and down the bus-crammed Amhurst Road towards his office in Stoke Newington. He normally conducted meetings in his Finest Office in Dalston but today he fancied a change. He hadn't been to Stoke Newington before. He'd heard strange things about it, mainly from his neighbours, but he wanted to see it first hand.

It was a long walk so Craig amused himself by mentally saluting every Mini-Store he walked past, thankful for their convenience. He couldn't remember what was there before the Minis started being built – probably some crusty cafés or sweaty music venues. The Minis were a constant reassurance that he was never too far from the Store.

The morning's important meeting went really well. Craig took his traditional victory walk. Normally, he would walk around Dalston grinning secretly to himself before walking into a Store and buying a sandwich.

However, after fifteen minutes looking for a Store in Stoke Newington, Craig began to panic. His stomach bubbled. He couldn't believe there wasn't even a Mini-Store in this place. How could people here live without Finest Sandwiches for lunch, or watching Finest Films in the evening? He pulled his Fine-Phone out to locate the nearest Store.

'Damn thing!' he cursed as he realised that he had forgotten to leave it to charge last night. Craig's hands turned moist. What was he going to eat?

Where was he going to find food? He couldn't go the whole journey back to his office on an empty stomach; he'd probably faint in this heat and be taken to the Value Hospital in Homerton. The horror. He'd have to just get a sandwich from somewhere else. Somewhere unqualified. Somewhere without the trusted flavours of the Finest ingredients. He ran up and down the leafy backstreets off Church Street, hoping he would somehow stumble across a Store. The more Craig ran, the more he got lost.

Eventually, he stopped running and sat on a bench to rest. Over the road, some sort of vile little independent sandwich bar was plying its trade. Exhausted, Craig didn't have the energy to be disgusted at the people going in and out, carrying handmade baguettes stuffed with fillings that contain absolutely no mayonnaise. Dejectedly, he shuffled into the sandwich bar and stared at the food on offer. He pointed at the BLT baguette and a lady, an actual person, picked it up with her bare hands and wrapped it in some paper. Trying not to retch, Craig paid for the baguette and quickly left the bar.

Back on the bench he ate the baguette.

And what a baguette.

Craig had never tasted anything like it. The crispiness of the smoky bacon was delectable. The tomato was so full of flavour and juice, so clean and fresh tasting. The lettuce actually had flavour rather than just being a textural addition to the filling as he'd always assumed it was. And the bread. Oh the bread! It was the softest, butteriest most beautifully tasting bread. The very outer crust crumbled away as he bit into it, leading him into a soft fluffy core that melted away in his mouth. Craig's senses were overloading, overpowering and overcoming him. He leaped up off the bench. He went back for another one.

Just as Craig put his right foot forward into the road with a purposeful and powerful stride his vision obscured. Without warning, a white plastic bag flew straight into his face and stuck there. Craig wrestled with it and began to lose his bearings, veering out into the middle of the road. Trying to pull the bag away from his face he began to lose his balance, stumbling from side to side. He was just about to wrench the thing away when he caught sight of the three familiar blue stripes and the red lettering of the Store. Then from the left, a Store Van crashed right into Craig's side, knocking him out cold.

When he came round, body aching and his vision blurry, Craig found himself tied to a white chair in the middle of a white room with three blue stripes running straight down the centre. There was no furniture, no windows and nobody else. He was stripped down to his underpants. No, wait – they weren't his underpants. He was wearing Value Underpants. His balls suddenly started to itch like crazy in protest. He tried to scratch them but he realised he couldn't move his hands. He looked round to see his hands in shackles, pinned to the wall.

A door opened in the white wall opposite Craig, a man and a woman entered the room. They strolled over to him, laughing to each other. Craig, confused and disorientated, started to laugh too. The man was in a Finest Suit, sporting a side parting in his greying, slicked down hair. He must have used Finest Gel, thought Craig, because the hair didn't look as if it was going to move any time soon. The woman, slightly taller than the man, had a frizz of red hair atop a freckly face. Her powder pink Finest Power Suit looked crisp and fresh, it reminded Craig of the bacon in his divine baguette.

'Now now, Craig Brewster. Stop laughing,' the woman said softly. 'How did you get here?'

'I... er, I don't know,' Craig replied, 'one minute I was eating the most incredible baguette I have ever tasted and the next I wake up here.'

'Where did you get the baguette from Craig, my love?'

'From Stoke Newington, there was this little independent sandwich bar thing called Al's Fres –'

'Ah, yes – Al's Fresco, yes we know about that place don't we Doctor Griskal? We know about Al's Fresco.'

The woman grit her teeth as she spat out the innocuous sounding shop name. She looked like she was about to get very angry but, seemingly checking herself, she shook an exaggerated shiver down her spine and plastered a smile onto her face. And a fine smile it was, reminiscent of the smiling check-out lady on the pay screens at the Store Arena.

'Do you know why you're here, Craig?' the woman continued without letting Craig answer. 'I will tell you. You are here because after all we've done for you, you still chose to eat the product of an "Independent Retailer".'

She paused to perform air quotes.

'You chose not only to eat the product of an "Independent Retailer", but you dared to enjoy the product of an "Independent Retailer". And beyond that, even more, you maintain it is the best thing you have ever eaten in your entire life. Have you forgotten the Store's own Lasagne Sandwich – recently released and only £4?'

Craig looked up at this woman, her curly red hair bouncing up and down with an airy, free delight that betrayed the angry tremors of her voice. She was obviously under their spell. The magic Store spell that he had somehow been bewitched by since before he could remember. He knew what it was like to look down on the Value Folk; he knew what it was like to feel the superiority of Finest. She must think she's the Finest of the fine. He looked at her and he saw himself. Or rather, his previous self. Because since he had allowed that baguette onto his tongue he had experienced liberation. He felt free of all the pressures and the conforming and the buying, (oh the constant buying) and the Finest of everything. He knew it was all poppycock; he had tasted the rainbow and there was no going back. He had tasted fresh food prepared and cooked on the day of consumption. His taste buds had been rescued from their dreary, dull lives. He was emancipated in all the ways that she was not. Nothing she said could change that now.

'You think you're better than me don't you, Craig? You think that you're enlightened? That you've "seen the light"? Well you haven't. The only light you've seen is the fluorescent lights that we run your life with. You don't even have the first idea of what is going on.'

Craig snorted.

He was confident there wasn't anything they could do to him that would stop him now. They'd have to kill him to stop him moving out of his Finest Apartment to an independent property and eating independent food from one of the grocers in the local market he'd heard rumours about. He wouldn't set foot in any of the seventeen Mini-Stores in Hackney ever again. They couldn't force him into them. They couldn't do that. They wouldn't do that. They needed him.

The woman leaned into Craig,

'Oh don't think you're going to just move out when we return you. Ha. We've got something much more exciting in store.'

'You have?'

'Oh yes my love. Do you remember your last grocery bill from the Store?'

'Er... no. I never see it. It just comes out of my bank account. But it won't be from now on because —'

'Don't jump ahead of yourself sweetie. You've never seen any of your itemised bills since you moved into the Store Megaplex seven years ago. Would you like to see one now? Say, March to April 2010?'

Before Craig could answer in the affirmative, the woman put her hand down her shirt and inside her bra. She then whipped out a folded piece of paper and carefully opened it in front of Craig's eyes. She squatted down next to Craig, put an arm around him and began to read out the items.

'Pristine Porridge, £3. Arabica Ground Free Trade Colombian Coffee: Hand picked by organically reared workers, £4.20. Finest of the Fine, Taste the Brilliant Difference, Sumptuous Sardinian Sardines in Organised Tomato Sauce, £8 per pack. Five packs purchased. Total, £40. Forty pounds on sardines Craig! Dear me. Two-kilogram packet of BasMagic Rice: Cooks instantly like toast, £6. One bottle of Châteaux Neuf du Pape. 2012 Vintage, £89. Crikey, I hope you got her in bed for that price. One-litre bottle of Finest Milk from cows that graze in the middle of the Stonehenge Circle, for an extra spiritual flavour, £7.90 –'

'Stop!' Craig cried out.

He didn't want to hear anymore of his previous labelled lunacy, his branded buffoonery. He looked down at his feet. Had he really spent all that money on this stuff?

'All right, Craig. All right, it's okay. There, there.'

She stroked his face.

Craig glanced over at the man, Dr Gacksil or whatever his name was. The doctor was leaning against the white wall, playing on a Finest Handheld Computer Game. His starch white lab coat blended into the wall so well, it looked like it was sucking him in. He was very involved with the game.

'I may have spent all that money,' said Craig, 'but at least I wasn't eating Value Food.'

'If only you knew,' the woman half whispered, 'but all in good time. Let's just have a look at the Value Bill of a typical Value Person shall we? Just for the sake of bi-partisanship. I wouldn't want you thinking that I hadn't been fair.'

'Fine.'

'Let's see...Value Pops, 50p. Value Fish Fingers: Trawled from unsustainable seas, £1. Value Weicz, a synthetic rice substitute, four kilogram bag, £1.20. Coffee, unfairly traded, 79p. I could go on—'

'Well, no – you can stop. I know it's cheaper. Much cheaper. Everyone knows that. But I still wouldn't—'

'Do you know how much your precious baguette was Craig?'

'No.'

'It was £4.50. That's a lot of money.'

'But it was delicious. It was out of this world.'

'That maybe the case Craig, believe me, that may have been the case. But look here.'

The woman pulled out a Fine-Phone from her jacket pocket and fiddled with it. She put it in front of Craig and waited for something to happen. Soon enough, a live video stream came up on the screen. Craig recognised the location – it was that street in Stoke Newington. There, framed directly in the middle, was Al's Fresco. The girl who served him was outside the front windows, sobbing, with lettuce in her hair and honey and mustard sauce splashed all down her top. Baguette rolls and fresh produce were strewn all over the road. A banner slowly unfurled over the shop sign. It revealed the words:

*Your local Mini-Store coming soon!*

'You're kidding me.'

'No Craig, I'm not. This is part of our nationwide roll-out. Hackney is a prime location, a population increasing in wealthy newcomers with no emotional ties to the established independent shops already in existence. It was a fair deal. We gave them an offer they couldn't refuse. Namely, that we'd choke their supply chain, set a store up next to them, undercut their prices and do them out of business. They were better off selling to us.

'Look at poor Independent Girl there. She looks so ugly when she cries. What's she going to do now? Probably try and run a stall at some well-meaning farmer-cooperative-backed "Artisanal

Food Market" and only ever break even. She'll probably go under because her tomato plant gets eaten by bugs. Who cares?'

'But why?'

'Oh never mind why. I'm not going to explain everything. This isn't an episode of *Poirot*, even if it is a master-stroke of cultural crime. I've got more to show you. Doc – put that silly game away, come on.'

Doctor Griskal peeled himself away from the clutches of the wall and followed the woman and Craig out through a door opposite the one they had come through. They walked down a long white corridor with three blue stripes running up and down the walls in a psychedelic swirl. After a couple of bewildering minutes, filled with the sound of the Doctor's tuneless humming of *Love Is All Around* they arrived at a door. The woman pushed it open and invited Craig to walk in.

As his eyes adjusted to the gloom of the room, Craig saw that they had entered an extremely efficient factory. Dimly lit brown conveyor belts whizzed round at high speeds carrying a staggering variety of produce. Everything available for sale at the Store was flashing past his eyes. The noise of the machinery was drowned out by the theme music to 1990s cult games show *Supermarket Sweep* on loop. Craig felt dizzy trying to concentrate on what he was looking at. He turned back to the woman. She smiled benignly and pointed him in the direction of the "Packaging Zone", a better lit and less frantic area to the left of the giant room. Timorously, he walked over and peered at the convoluted machines which were wrapping up and labelling the produce.

The exact same minced meat leaving the mincer and travelling along the belts was going into the Value packets and the Finest packets at the very end. The exact same milk was being labelled "Value" and "Finest". The potatoes were rumbling past indiscriminately into sacks marked "Value" and "Finest".

Craig watched in astounded silence as every product he could think of was packaged in two different ways but without changing its biological constitution whatsoever. He looked back over the factory and back along the conveyor belts just to check he wasn't seeing it wrong. It was then that he noticed the huge pictures hanging all over the factory walls. Hundreds of pictures of agricultural farms, with a red line plastered through them saying "Acquired" or "Gotcha!"

'I don't understand. What am I supposed to do now?' Craig cried out across the factory floor, his mind reeling. In Stoke Newington he thought he'd experienced the sublime but now he was faltering under the crushing weight of realism and inevitability.

'There isn't much you can do.'

'The v-v-v-v-Value, it's the same as the—'

'Yes, the same as the Finest. It's all the in the mind Craig. If you make people believe something tastes better, they will convince themselves it does. Think of the money you save Craig. Think about the bargains. Imagine the reduction of our products to pure, unadulterated buying pleasure, without the physical product changing whatsoever. Think of the fact that you can buy one-and-a-half kippers for breakfast for 50p. You can buy Value Bacon for £1. You could reduce your weekly shopping bill by up to eighty per cent, but you could consume twice as much. You could save for your future children, you could feed your future family for much less than a fiver. There would be more reasons to shop at the Store, the pence make the pounds, spend money to make money. There's really no point in trying to join the other cretins out in their pointless independent world, you'll just lose money and time. And, I'll tell you what, I'll give you this.'

The woman pulled out her wallet and slid a card out. It was

gold plated and had "SuperStoreCard" emblazoned on the front.

'This,' she said, placing it in Craig's palm, 'gets you one hundred times the amount of reward points a normal StoreCard does on every single purchase.'

Craig wrapped his fingers around the card and stood in silence. The sound of Dale Winton's voice singing, 'Check it out, check it out,' swirled around him. She was right of course, he had been shopping like a sucker before. He'd been getting ripped off. Had she rescued him? Had she saved him? What was in this for her? Were they rewarding him for stepping outside the Store box?

He thought of the consumer knowledge he had just been given access to. The inside scoop on the branded products, the wisdom of the super shopper. He could be the ultimate super shopper, the best value, most conscious consumer that the Store had ever seen. He could save so much money. He could save for his and his future wife's future Store children, and for their future Store children. He could save for whatever the future had in Store. He could hand down years of learned consumer knowledge to his children, helping them navigate their way around this crazy world like the erudite father he always dreamed of being. He had never felt happier to be involved with the Store in his life.

He looked at the woman. 'Thank you,' he mouthed silently.

'No problem,' she replied. A bright and warm smile flushed over her face.

'Looks like he wants to go back, doesn't it, Doc?'

'It sure does,' mumbled Doctor Griskal from somewhere in the room.

'I do. I do want to go back! I want to stock my fridge up, find a bargain suit and take that girl in the flat next door out for a slap up, steal of a dinner at the Store Tandoori.'

The woman slapped Craig on the back.

'Stick it to him Doc,' she shouted at Griskal.

Dr Griskal opened his briefcase and brought out a syringe, filled with a translucent liquid. He raised his monobrow at Craig. Craig nodded, he knew they wouldn't ever allow him to see how he got to this place, but he would never forget what he'd learned inside. The Doctor put the Value Syringe into his arm and pushed down the plunger. Craig felt woozy, then dizzy, then spinning.

Then darkness arrived.

***

Craig leaped out of his Value Bed and rushed to put on his Value Pyjamas. He ran down the stairs in excitement noting down the advice his door gave him on the way out, 'We have a special on Value Beans and Kippers this morning Craig – go get 'em tiger!'

Craig entered the Store and ran over to his designated bag in the Breakfast Aisle. He pulled out every delicious item one by one and sniffed each one lovingly. His neighbour, Jessica was up early too, 'Those Kippers are gorgeous aren't they Craig?' she called over from the next aisle.

'They sure are Jessica! I love Value Kippers in the morning, and such a bargain. They're so cheap I'm going to buy twenty packets, eat four and throw away the rest!'

Craig flashed her an ecstatic smile. He really meant it. He'd loved these Value Kippers ever since he could remember. In fact he loved all the Value Store items they ever made. Each one was an absolute giveaway of a price.

Craig put his items back in his bag and set off for the long, lovely walk to the check-out. Just before his first step though, Craig suddenly got the creepy sensation that someone was watching him. He turned around and looked straight at the mirror that ran the length of the Store Arena. He stared closely into the mirror – his own reflection staring back at him with equal intensity. He could have sworn that for a moment he saw another Store, a different Store on the other side of the mirror with other people walking around inside picking up produce, the same produce he had but in different packages. He leaned forward and tapped the glass, not knowing what he was expecting to happen.

Nothing happened.

Craig laughed at himself for being so stupid and skipped off down towards the check-out. How could there be another Store in this building? This was the only Store here he'd ever known. It was his home, his provider, his counsel and his mentor. The Value Mini-Stores were his guiding lights in the outside world. He was so lucky to be one of the most Valued customers. So lucky to be one of the chosen few and have such a brilliant company looking after all the important things, so he didn't have to. The people on the outside at the dirty markets and the shared houses, they must be miserable.

The Store made sure everything was all right. Recommending meals every evening, suggesting films to watch and books to read. The Store was making sure he got the best deals every day. The Store knew him inside out and he couldn't imagine a future without it by his side.

# 'Ackney

*By Isaura Barbé-Brown*

If I had to pick the place that knows me best, I'd pick here.
It's not the glorious love affair some people pretend to have
with their town.
The streets aren't paved with gold, in fact more often than not
They're paved with dog shit.
I have no rose tinted glasses.
I'm no band-wagon-jumper-onner.

Even now I sit across from my parent's wedding picture taken on
an autumn day outside St. John at Hackney.
The same place my brother and I were baptised months after we
were born at Mother's hospital, for those who remember.
I went to school at Berger where I learnt how to be a good kid
who never got caught.
And where I fell for my first Frenchman.
Hey Jules.
A habit I'm yet to break.

I skinned my knees in Vicky Park where I learnt to ride my bike,

The bike I got from E. Gibbons that lives on only in memories.

The chemist and the grocer have known me by name since I was knee high to nothing.

When I was sick I was nursed back to health at The Queen Elizabeth,

With strawberry jelly, cabbage patch dolls and *Lady and the Tramp*.


I've seen dark days. A man knifed, another shot and for what? Usually nothing.

The Murder Mile, a name that stuck for good reason.

These things, though dark, are not our secrets but our scars.

Some of them ugly,

But healed or healing all the same.

Nobody's perfect.


I love the bumps and cracks of this place.

I'm an original.

I'm in every nook and cranny.

I love it, heart and soul even when I hate it.

Every time we have a fight and I throw a tantrum and leave for foreign lands,

When I return, as I always do, it's to open arms.

And as I nestle back in to its familiar streets and faces, it holds me closer and says,

'Welcome home'.

# Suki's Cherry

*By Georgia Myers*

An invite to the party would mean getting close to Marcus, closer than just brushing past each other between last lessons on a Friday.

Suki slid exercise books into her dark, purple bag, stealing sidelong glances at him, slumped forward on his French desk, eyes all sleepy.

She felt Mon's eyes on her. She looked away quickly, feeling heat blooming on her cheeks.

'You have to come to the party; we need to get you set up.'

Her best friend gestured to Marcus.

'But I'm not invited,' Suki whispered.

'I'll ask Sabrina about you coming, it's the perfect opportunity.'

Mon was like a sister. She lent Suki money and decent clothes and kept everything about her home life a secret.

'Is Sharon Allen going?' she asked her fearfully.

'Probably.'

Even the teachers were scared of Marcus' ex-girlfriend. Sharon

Allen would definitely beat her up if she found out their plan.

During third lesson Suki felt an unruly wetness in her knickers. She slid a sanitary towel expertly up her sleeve and asked permission to go to the toilet. She smelt something burning even before she pushed open the door. She was inside. It was too late.

Sharon Allen was sitting on the edge of one of the sinks, cigarette in her mouth, a laugh in her eye. She sucked deeply, took it from her lips with a thumb and forefinger, like a cowboy. She had an old face. Her eyes black with eye-liner, hair in a top knot, the black polo neck consciously not school uniform.

'Want a drag, Chicken Legs?' she spoke with an old husky voice.

'No thanks.'

Suki ducked into the cubicle and started changing her pad. She flushed the toilet. As the gurgling died away she noticed Sharon Allen looking down over the partition, laughing.

'Put your nappy on then?' Smoke blurted from her mouth. 'Never done IT, eh?'

Her virginity felt like a bad outfit her mum had bought in a charity shop – out of date and unflattering. Suki straightened up, held a breath, listening for silence. She unlocked the door and washed her hands. Suddenly hands clasped her shoulders, fingers dug into her collarbone. Sharon's husky whisper came in her ear.

'You're a dirty squatter. I've seen all the crusty people coming in and out of your house. It's disgusting.' The girl jumped back laughing. 'Only joking, only joking Chicken Legs. C'mon,' she smiled, pushing Suki's shoulder.

How did she know everything? Suki smiled back. It was not worth upsetting her.

Sharon Allen pushed her fag butt down the plughole.

'Anyway you're coming to Sabrina's party – I've told her you are coming. And by the way – men are dogs, you'll see.'

Suki swallowed hard, watching the girl bounce off, quaking at the idea of walking through Holly Street estate, of seeing Marcus out of school. But this was her chance. She would have to get some money somehow, go up Ridley Market on Saturday morning and buy something to wear, something red, preferably Lycra.

Suki managed to borrow some money off someone sleeping on their sofa, to wheedle out of the communal bonfire party in her garden, where they were burning an effigy of Margaret Thatcher and eating veggie hot dogs. She had scrunch-dried her hair. She left, unseen, through the basement door.

They were meeting outside the Chinese on Queensbridge Road. The cold night air smelt of gunpowder. Goose bumps covered Suki's arms and legs, distracting her from the prickly terror in her intestines.

Sharon Allen was leant up against the glass of the Chinese with a can of Super Tennents in one hand, the other planted in her pocket. She only ever wore trousers and long sleeves. Mon said it was to hide the bruises.

'Hi, Sharon.'

'Hey Chicken Legs, looking good.' She circled Suki, appraising her like a man would. Suki pulled down the back of her new dress. She rubbed her cerise-pink lips together. If she could not handle the glare of Sharon Allen, how would she cope in front of Marcus? Please let him be there.

'Here y'are.' Sharon Allen thrust the can at her. She tried to take an expert gulp, just managing to contain the warm filthy tasting liquid.

'Aarrgh! It's like tramp's piss!'

Sharon Allen laughed.

'You'll get used to it.' She drained the can, crumpled it up and chucked it, narrowly missing an old woman at the bus stop.

'You fancy Marcus, innit?' She squinted.

'Not really.'

'You do, don't lie, I'm gonna set you up. He likes you, I asked him. It's time to pop your cherry, Chicken.'

'But I thought –'

Round the corner came Mon, purple faced and puffing in her turquoise sailor suit, legs marbled with cold.

'Sorry I'm late, mum made me stay till the end of dinner. Got a fag Sha?'

How could Sharon Allen have known about Marcus? Suki looked afresh at the full figure of her mate. Surely Mon would not have told her. That didn't matter now. She hardly dared believe it! He liked her. Her flesh felt sweet and ripe. She was ready.

'C'mon – we got a party to go to.' Sharon Allen bowled ahead, doing a short skip with each step on the left leg.

As they walked through the estate, aromas of curry, fried food and rubbish mingled with muffled shouting, Greek music, a baby crying. A gang of teenage boys sat on a wall by a tatty football pitch. A couple were older boys from school. No sign of Marcus. Sharon Allen went over, smoked with them, stroked the hands of a couple. The boys were still and composed, only nodding measured greetings.

'Oh my God, it's Curtis Reid!' gasped Mon. 'He's gorgeous!'

Suki rolled her eyes.

'Sorted.' Sharon Allen returned squeezing her eyes and patting her pocket.

Deeper into the brick and concrete they went, climbed the stairs to a fourth-floor walkway, on past front doors, some with grilles, one barricaded up. Suki was thrilled. She was going to a party. A party that was not at her house, that would definitely not include a birthday cake, a party where he would be waiting.

Sharon Allen marched up to a door with lacy curtains behind shatterproof glass. Smoke curled out of the window and loud ragga music rocked a china ornament on the sill. Sharon Allen leant on the bell with her thumb then immediately started shouting 'Oi' through the letterbox.

'Oi, Sabrina, you chief, open the door!'

The door opened a crack and Sabrina's slim brown face with dizzy owl eyes appeared, a tall boy's face perched on top of hers.

'Alright Sharon, alright Monica.' she looked Suki up and down. 'I never invited her.'

Suki felt like diving off the walkway right there, except her mum would find out she was not really staying at Mon's, watching *Take Me Out*.

Sharon Allen's arm came draping around her shoulders.

'She's alright man, she's my mate. Open the door.'

'I don't want none of her in my house.'

'C'mon. Move. Tell Daffy I got something for him. Daff!' she shouted through the crack.

Another head appeared in the doorway, beneath Sabrina's, completing the human traffic light.

'Let them in. C'mon 'Rina, don't be moody.' Daffy forced open the door. The tall boy carried Sabrina off, skinny legs kicking.

Mon and Sharon stepped into the small carpeted hallway, Suki hesitated. Sharon Allen took her wrist and yanked her inside, hustled her past the brass horse shoes hanging on the wall and straight into the toilet.

'What are you doing?' Suki's voice deadened, in the tiny windowless room. She backed up against the door.

'Watch this.' Sharon Allen took a small rectangle of paper from her pocket, unfolded it, took a pinch of white powder from inside, put it on the back of her hand and sniffed it up her right nostril, making a sudden snort, pulling her body up tall.

'Right, listen up. I'm gonna give you some tips. Don't let him rough you up. You want to be treated like a lady.' She did a little twirl, wiggling her bum and laughing.

'Kissing and taking it slow and all that. Now if he gets a bit fruity, take this.'

She tucked a silver, foil square into Suki's cleavage.

'Don't forget to pinch the end when you're rolling it on.'

'But—'

'You want a toot?'

'No.'

'Didn't think so. Wasn't going to give you anyways,' she sneered.

Suki scanned the living room, then the brightly lit kitchen, no sign of him. On the table were bottles of cider, Peach Canai and own-brand vodka. She found a used plastic cup, rinsed it out and poured something into it, stretching out the action. Her dress felt very short, too tarty.

A couple of guys in Puffa jackets and sunglasses were leant up against the countertop nodding in time to the loud hip hop. Suki tried to look mysterious, serious, whilst casting her eye over the neat kitchen, with its orderly nest of wicker fruit baskets, kitchen roll with sunflowers on, framed Home Sweet Home embroidery. Different to her own grubby kitchen strewn with bicycle parts, anarchist newspapers and squashed raisins.

'Y'alright?' One of the guys jerked his head back.

'Yeah cool.'

'You the gal Marcus is chirps-ing innit?'

She felt her cheeks firing up to scarlet. She tried to perch seductively on the work surface, the booze starting to course through her system.

One of the guys turned to the other.

'I saw him heading over Clapton sides. Is he coming?'

'Nah, doubt it.'

She tried to elevate herself. Her hand slipped. She clattered to the floor hitting her elbow and shoulder, legs splayed.

The two guys creased over, crying with laughter. She crawled away into the hallway, humiliation and pain biting in equal measure. At least Marcus had not witnessed her fall. She hoiked her dress down, took a deep breath and went into the living room.

There was a small huddle of people dancing. It felt a bit absurd now, here in Sabrina's family living room, the three-piece suite had plastic covers on, the wall of mahogany plywood shelves, the hi-fi being guarded by two older-looking boys, who didn't go Kingsland. The one with a V-shaped slice out of his ear fitted the description of the notorious Danny Horatio.

Monica was dancing with Daffy. She smiled at Suki over his shoulder, then buried her head in his neck. If only Suki had half Mon's guts. She looked around. It was all pointless without Marcus coming.

She felt a pair of arms circle her waist from behind, felt someone's belt pushing into her back, the sickly smell of aftershave. It was Steven Henry, a boy in her class. She turned round, draped her arms around his shoulders. As she did so a leering cheer rose from the hem of the tiny dance floor.

There was Marcus in the doorway. He clocked her and turned back. Suki's chest tightened, she wanted to run after, tell him, touch him. But her feet shuffled heavily in a slow circle with

Steven Henry. What if he thought she was not interested?

The next song was a faster one, she fell back on the sofa, hoping Marcus would come back to the room, come and sit next to her. Instead Steven sat down, turned his body to her, put a coke bottle to her lips.

'Hey baby, feelin' the chemistry between us?' He tipped the bottle.

'Sorry Steven.' She pushed it away.

'What ya sayin?' You like me innit?' His tongue flicked in and out of his mouth.

'Not really.' Her thighs were sticking to the plastic covers.

'Come on baby, we're good together.' He tried to move closer and slide his arm around her.

'Get off.' She got up and went into the kitchen, searching.

Sharon Allen's face was pushed up against hers, breath hot and vinegary.

'Someone's outside waiting to talk to you. Come on, he's my mate and he likes you. It's easy.'

Suki's blood herded around her body, alerting every nerve, every extremity to the oncoming confrontation. This was it! How could Sharon Allen do this to her? She hated her, she loved her. They headed out into the night. Leaning over the walkway Sharon Allen pointed to the lone figure on the wall, slouched and moody looking.

'Go on then.' Her face was pure, even kind, like a lonely bulldog. What was she up to?

Wobbling, she held the rail and headed down the concrete stairs to the open space below. Everything was going to be different from now on. She had to concentrate so hard on putting one foot in front of the other, it felt alien.

'I've forgotten how to walk!' she blurted, arriving in front of him.

'Really?' He looked bemused. 'How much have you had to drink?'

'It's not that. It's... well maybe it is that. I've had a few vodkas, beers, some –'

'Sit down.'

Her heart was thrashing around like a fish in a net. They had already exchanged more words than ever before.

'What did Sharon Allen say to you?'

'Not much. What did she say to you?' He scratched the back of his neck.

They looked at each other sideways. He had a lop-sided smile, twinkly green eyes, dark freckles.

They looked away, made shy by the naked eye contact.

'I've been wanting to talk to you.' He shuffled closer, cupped her face in his hands. Suki willed her body to co-operate.

'You're hot.' He leant in, touched his nose and lips to her face.


The night was crackling, alive.

A gang of young kids skidded past, dropping something at their feet. It hissed and snaked around on the ground, yellow, orange sparks flying out of its back.

Suki felt herself pushed hard on the chest and fell back over the wall onto the soft cold grass, biting her lip as she did so. Red and blue sparks spat over the wall, followed by bangs. They shuffled backwards laughing in fright, clutching each other.

'Bloody hell, you little bastards!' Marcus shouted and laughed, all the time staring into her eyes.

People from the party spilled out on the walkway above.

'Are you alright?' Mon called, running down the stairs. 'Oh my God, you could have been killed!'

She knelt down and looked at Marcus, took his hands and cocked her head to one side.

'Are you sure you're alright?'

Suki licked at the iron tasting blood.

'Oh my God, Suki, you're bleeding. Come inside quickly.' Mon pulled Suki's arm. Her strength had Suki on her feet instantly. She was dragged off, throwing a forlorn look back to Marcus. He stood reaching out a hand.

Suki sat on the toilet seat whilst Monica fussed over her lip, dousing her with more vodka and TCP, pulling her hair back into a scraggy ponytail. The little room was starting to rock.

'You better come and lie down Su, you don't want Marcus seeing you really pissed.' Mon led her into a bedroom, to a soft, mauve double bed.

She flopped back. Mon was right, better sober up a bit. Her head span with thrilling images of her and Marcus – sitting on the wall, sharing portions of chips at lunchtime, kissing on Hackney Downs, maybe even doing it! She hugged herself, drifted off.

\*\*\*

The door burst open.

'Oi – what's happening?'

The gruff tone of Sharon Allen's voice roused her. Heavy presences either side of her sprang off the bed.

'Get out, what you doing? You slag! This is my mum's bed, you're taking liberties.' Sabrina waved her arms around.

Suki sat up, felt her bra unhooked, the straps of her stained dress round her elbows. Confused, she hugged herself, squeezing the flesh of her arms.

Against the window the silhouette of Danny Horatio, gold rings glinting as he flexed the muscles in his forearms. He made a long sucking noise against his teeth and bounded out of the room.

To her left Steven Henry, grinning, doing up his trousers. The smell of fresh sweat. Bile turned over in her gut. As he stood up Sharon Allen kneed him in the balls.

'Your mum's got horns.' She spat on him. 'Move, you scum.' He scurried off.

She sat on bed next to Suki, held her chin and looked into her face.

'You're alright Chicken Legs, looks like I was just in time eh?' She picked up the intact foil square from Suki's lap.

'I know those types, always looking to take.'

Deep in Sharon Allen's steely eyes Suki thought she detected a glimmer of pain, even sadness.

Suki staggered off, she had to find Mon. They had to get out of here. The music had been turned up even louder and the living room grown to bursting, people knocking into each other and shaking their heads, lost in the heavy bass lines.

She felt woozy, disorientated in the fog, bumped into a tangle of legs; the bare legs and turquoise skirt of her oldest friend. Relief. She peered at the figure beneath Mon. Black t-shirt, baggy jeans. Her hopes drained away, her world reshuffled. Monica, with wild candyfloss hair, looked straight past her, leant down and snogged Marcus.

Suki turned, her heart hanging out. She folded her arms over her stomach, willing herself not to cry, sucking her emotions back in. She thought of the photo on her mantelpiece of her and Mon as little girls in Hyde Park, on a sunny CND march.

The dancers made a circle around her in which she span,

looking at the strange, laughing faces, the sliced ear, the guys with sunglasses, a girl with an armful of bangles, all strobing past. It felt like they were goading her, pointing, clapping slowly.

She pushed through the ring and out into the hall, out onto the walkway, her footsteps echoing against concrete.

Golden showers bloomed high in the far off sky.

She got down to the wall, where things had looked so different, so recently.

Sitting on it was Sharon Allen again.

'C'mon, I'm walking you home Chicken Legs.'

It had grown late and cold. Suki's arms hung deflated by her sides, her stomach like a stone.

'They're all only after one thing.'

'You got it.' Sharon nodded. She hopped off the wall.

'Let's go get some chips, go back to yours. I've always wanted to go inside that madhouse.'

They linked arms and walked off into the smoke-filled night.

# All Gone

*By Andrea Watts*

This was the second time the girl had stuck her card into the machine. Clearly there was no money in the account. Jamie looked away and tried to slow his breathing. The cashpoint was wedged in the corner of a supermarket wall, some distance from the entrance. In addition, some clown had parked their four-by-four in front of the machine. The only way out was through the same narrow passage you came in by. The girl was leaning her head against the wall and joggling her buggy. He wondered if there was something wrong with her or if she was being slow just to wind him up. Tapping his card against his wallet, he moved closer.

Her baby stared up at him. It was a bald little imp with oversized ears, and eyes that were too dark and knowing. It was dressed in pink frills and had dirty bare feet. He grimaced and it nodded back, threw out its arms, dropped its doll – a raggedy thing, with a starched black bonnet – and said, 'All gone!'

Yes. All gone. Now get out the way.

But the girl was still punching numbers. What was she up to? He watched her arse twitch. It was perky, propped up by a tight white skirt trailing a thread. Bare legs, shapely enough, but let down by their blue-grey hue. They sort of glowed, like the light shone from within.

Come on.

Her little toe was poking through the straps of her yellow sandals. The nail was long and jagged. She hadn't bothered to paint it. An extractor fan above them started pumping out hot dry air and she shook the buggy harder. Her Iceland bag scraped the ground, making a ragged hole. He could see a packet of frozen veg poking through and had a vision of her skating, cartoon-like, on a rolling carpet of peas.

The card was rejected again. She slipped it in her back pocket. Whirs and clunks sounded. Something was happening. The machine was spitting notes, five, six, seven... he shifted his weight to get a better look. The pile was getting higher. Were they fifties? Must be thirty of them. She must be clearing out the boyfriend's account. Or perhaps a client's. Or some bigger fraud, like she'd hacked into the bank's mainframe.

The notes stopped. Ten centimetres of them. Another whir-clunk and a slip slid out. Clutching the paper she studied it. Her face was kite-shaped, her eyes liquid bright; she looked as vulnerable as a baby bird. She turned, grabbed her buggy and backed out. As she brushed against him, he leant in to smell her – sweat and talc and something else. His Nan's house, perhaps her budgie. Not its cage though. More like the smell of the air as it beat its wings against the window. The smell passed and he opened his eyes. She had gone. But her wodge of cash was still in the tray. Without checking behind him, he put his own card in the slot, punched his numbers and watched a twenty fall on her pile. Then he slipped the stack in his inside jacket pocket.

A decisive can-doer without conscience, he hummed. A player

without remorse. Christ, he'd be running the country soon.

As he continued down the High Road, a slant of yellow light appeared between the filthy buildings on his left. It blinded him momentarily before disappearing. There followed a flash of black; a flutter like the beating of a rug. He had to duck. Some damn crow. No. One of those magpies. Shit. That was close. Yah! He stamped in its direction and the magpie hopped lazily onto the roof of a blue Mini, tipped its tail feather and slid white slop down the windscreen. The day got better and better.

When he reached his bus stop, the notes were tingling against his chest. How much would there be, four grand? Eight? More if they were all fifties. Bingo!

The day felt close. He flapped his jacket to create some air. He looked at the sky. Blue. Vast. Clouds like horses' tails. A bus pulled up followed by a surge of people, pushing and touching, diesel to make you sick. Jamie hopped away from them, shaking his head. He'd skip work today. Head south to the river. He was in too good a mood to be cooped up with losers and slaves.

As he walked, the houses got bigger, the roads wider. This was Bonus Land. This was his future. This little sweetener in his pocket was just the start. He could feel the wind picking up, pushing him forward. He broke into a run, keeping away from main roads, dodging contact with people. The cash was weighing on him, dragging him to one side. He kept moving. He bypassed the City, cut through blocks of estates and onto the canal path, where the wind was still.

He checked there was no one about and put his hand into his pocket. Instead of the dry touch of so many notes, his fingers slipped against something slimy and something that tickled. He yanked his hand back, pulling out a puff of feathers and a smell of farmyard. Bird shit. He clawed at his jacket and beat it to the ground. Ripping at the lining he saw that the money had gone. He'd been had. She must have been watching him, following him. Somehow she swapped the money for this stinking stuff. He looked over his shoulder for hidden cameras, for talk show hosts. The notes couldn't have been real. A scam. A plot to get his bank details; but he couldn't understand how. He was missing something. The shit was expanding. It was dripping out of his pockets. He could feel it cold against his skin. His trouser button burst and more dark feathers exploded forth, dimming the light. As they settled they clung to him, puncturing the skin and taking root. Hopping and shivering he tore at the remaining fabric and levered off his ruined shoes. He tripped and fell, knocking one of them into the water. Five coots took to the sky and he strained to follow them. He crawled to an old brick bridge and hid himself. He ripped at his shirt until it hung over his back attached by the idle noose of his blue silk tie. Huddled naked, except for the cloak, he scratched his new feathers against the wall.

\*\*\*

Colour is seeping from the light. Emmeline and the baby on whom she dotes stand holding hands. They have followed their man, their songless blackbird, along the canal to the east of the city. He is hidden trembling and flapping against the wall of a viaduct. When he ceases to move, Emmeline smiles. The baby laughs and claps and rocks on her bare feet. Emmeline picks her up, balancing her in the crook of her arm, so that she faces out.

They take a bus. Emmeline is unconcerned which one. It is crowded and she stands in the aisle, still holding the baby. A woman whose face is alight with aubergine curls, shoves past them, trailing a sweet clammy scent. When a seat becomes available she drops into it without looking up, head bent over a paperback. The baby turns to Emmeline and tugs her hair. She points to the woman, throws out her hands and drops the doll. 'Gone,' she coos. The woman crosses one leg over the other and they watch the fluttery-bounce of her free foot. Emmeline shrugs and gently, she lowers the baby into her buggy, picks up the doll and puts it on her lap. The baby's eyes sparkle, then droop; sparkle, droop, until her head falls back in a seraphic smile.

# VI

Homerton / Hackney Wick

# Foucault Over the Garden Fence

*By Eithne Nightingale*

'I was a nun with a very bad habit,' laughed Tony, pouring himself more vodka. 'My friend was the bishop and I would knock off his mitre and look up his hassock.'

'Cassock,' I ventured, thinking it must be the drink. It seemed improbable that my erudite neighbour, who spoke ten languages, should make such an elementary, ecclesiastical mistake.

'Then we set the mice free and the pious got up on their chairs screaming at God's furry little creatures scampering underneath. It was a riot.'

Tony was beside himself, doubling over at the memories of disrupting the Christian Festival of Light.

'Oh,' he suddenly exclaimed. 'I forgot you were a vicar's daughter. I hope I haven't offended you.'

'Not at all,' I smiled, tendering my glass for more vodka. 'I think my father might have approved.'

Tony had been my neighbour for fourteen years. Over the garden fence and between the leaves of the wisteria he talked to me of Foucault, feminism and far-left politics. And whilst the wisteria never flowered, our friendship did. Spring excursions to the auction house, summer walks along the River Lea, autumn trips to a gallery or two and convivial winter meals of broccoli soup and chocolate tiramisu. In the early morning light we fed the birds and late at night we argued politics over endless tumblers of Russian vodka.

Tony was always there for me when the going got tough; when my car tyres were slashed, my brake cable cut and my keyholes glued. I slept in his house warmed by hot toddies and macaroni cheese, safe from the fury of my ex-lover.

'All clear,' he would shout as he peered through the curtains. I would rush next door for a change of clothes and return to my refuge.

And he was there when I got burgled, my belongings scattered down the street as the thieves made their escape. After the third break-in within a month I talked of moving from our Hackney terraced street.

'You can't leave without me,' he cried.

Nudging, nurturing neighbours on the margins of Murder Mile.

And I was there for him when he needed a break from writing his book on the male nude in the eighteenth century.

'Hopeless,' he would sigh and I would listen, trying to dislodge his writer's block.

Tony was not only a member of the Gay Liberation Movement but an active campaigner in the early days of the squatting movement in London, occupying boarded houses left to rot by the local council. Once he told me how he had arranged bail for two East End lads living in the same squat as him. They were brothers who had lost their parents, fallen on hard times and taken to drugs.

'I took them home to my mother,' he said. 'They loved it and ate all her home-made cakes.'

I imagined the scenario. A respectable, middle-class lady from suburbia offering a Victoria sponge to her gay son and his jailbird friends, cosseted by chintz but nervous for her silver.

The one time we nearly came to blows was when Tony insisted I chop down the elderberry tree casting a shadow over the bottom of his garden. I procrastinated, offered to trim it back, tempted him with endless supplies of elderflower wine and elderberry jam.

'It must go,' he insisted. 'It is a plague on both our houses.'

Within days a lean, gay gardener from Abney cemetery scaled the branches, electric saw in hand and the tree was gone.

'Into darkness comes light,' announced Tony, cracking open a bottle of champagne.

Then one day everything changed. Tony, this sixty-year-old, handsome, bald and bearded academic fell terribly in love with a tall, full-faced, burly Polish waiter half his age who only spoke ten words of English.

'Stefan's not rung today,' he grumbled, emptying his vodka glass in one go.

I waited, anxious for the next installment.

'I went to see him at work but the restaurant owner threw me out,' he laughed, gazing at the portrait of his lover on his mobile phone.

But as the affair unfolded, there was anger at his lover's refusal to disclose his sexuality to family and friends.

'I will out him,' he cried, pacing around the garden.

'You can't do that. His mother's a devout Catholic.'

Tony beyond reason. Tony passionately in love.

One day his lover upped sticks and left for Poland and Tony's despair pervaded his tumbledown house. Shelves of leather-bound editions of Goethe, Byron, Proust lay neglected. Videos of *Porridge*, *The Simpsons* and *Cell Block H* remained unwatched. There were no late night political arguments over tumblers of vodka. No early morning feeding of the birds.

But two weeks later there was renewed excitement.

'Stefan's coming back with his sister, brother-in-law and nephew.'

The house was decorated. Apple green downstairs, fresh white for the hallway. A new carpet, sideboard and a giant plasma television screen. A buzz of domesticity. Cleaning, painting, cooking.

There were invitations to Polish Sunday lunch starting with borscht and ending with oodles of cream and historic walks round the East End of London with Tony as our guide.

'First there were the Huguenots, then the Jews from Poland fleeing the pogroms in the nineteenth century.' Tony laughed and brandished his arm towards his lover.

'And now we have the Poles again.'

He liked to show off his newly found passion to his friends; his friends to his newly found lover. There were trips to the social security offices to find out about benefits, visits to the nursery to secure a place for the nephew. Tony, the linguist, armed with a Polish dictionary, supporting and loving his newly adopted family. He asked all his friends to find work for Stefan so he could earn more than the minimum wage. So he could stay in England and with him.

But after a month and for no obvious reason, the Polish family left to live in West London. Student exam papers remained unmarked and the forthcoming book on nudity languished. I fabricated a reason for the estranged couple to meet and make up.

'I still need my bedroom decorating.'

So Stefan agreed but Tony wanted to interrupt his friend, to cook broccoli quiche and make love between the coats of paint. But his lover was focused on his task.

'I'm working.'

'If not now, when? Come tomorrow night.'

I worried as I travelled to see my family for the weekend, thinking I should ring to make sure Tony was all right. But something stopped me. A feeling I couldn't identify; a fear I didn't dare acknowledge.

I returned on the Sunday to a crackled answer phone message from my other neighbour.

'Call round when you get back. Something's happened to Tony.'

I knew straight away that he was dead. That it was suicide. Perhaps I was the only person who knew, besides his lover, that he would do it. Could do it. The police wanted to see me. Just to make sure it was not a murder. Just to make sure it was suicide.

Over the months that followed, each time I went into his house, the room where he killed himself, I felt his despair. Each time I picked up the American book lying on the table, *A Hundred Best Ways to Commit Suicide*.

I felt it. Felt his despair. I read and reread the suicide note written to his lover, long since gone.

'I'm sorry but I have never been so happy.'

The police had no problem tracking Stefan down. His mobile number was written on the suicide note.

As I emptied the house – prints and books to university libraries, household goods to the homeless and refugees, I thought of the students not taught, the book not written, the friendships fractured. Did all these mean so little in the wake of love? And where was Stefan? There was no sign or sight of him, just paint on my bedroom carpet as a lasting reminder.

It took some time to trace distant relatives, to find the will. Half of the estate was to go to the two brothers whom Tony had rescued from jail and taken to tea with his mother. But the will was out of date. One of the brothers had died of a drug overdose years ago.

I rolled back the film. Thought back to when I could have stopped this madness. But perhaps it was a considered act, a loss too hard to bear, too reminiscent of painful, past betrayals. Indeed, is this what we all risk in the pursuit of love? I tried hard to accept his death; respect his right to end his life. But still Tony is not there. Tony is not next door.

I chat to prospective new neighbours, pushing back the stubborn wisteria. Yes, the house is in a terrible state. Needs a complete makeover but it's a charming street and not far from the city. No talk of feminism or far-left politics. No Foucault over the garden fence.

# Dark Island:
# Wallis Road 09.03.11

*By Colin Priest*

From the north eastern point of Victoria Park to the Olympic
Valley,
A super-walkway is planned – Park-to-Park.

Brushing between the boundaries of Hamlets and Hackney,
Lies a northern road named Wallis.

Viewed from a fish bone bridge across the A12.
Nearly complete,
Some pedestrian works.
Arriving at Chapman's;
A cross, road.

Welcome to Wick.
A billboard and some wasteland,
A line of corrugated nests,
A sweet smell of aerosol and some damp mists.

Straight on.

Past White Post Lane, Wallis becomes a canyon.
Upright layers of candy brick and evergreens fortify the left.
Fragile and aged London Stock towers and slackens to the right.
Stacked behind, rusty skips;
McGrath's of London once a printers risk.

Tightly underfoot, a bright level grey concrete
Dusted, with a cosmetic.

Straight-ahead: Hackney Wick.
Orange formerly silver.
A ramp to Richmond or Junction,
Sometimes twenty minutes to Circus,
Sometimes not.

Underfoot a mini roundabout.
Far right, the landmark face of Lord Napier,
An old inn, now quicksilver for wicked screenings and alike.

Around the corner
Under the bridge.
To the left, a ramp up to the outer east:
Stratford.

Past the action plan site of special interest – the Lion Works,
Then the orange convenience store and one-time Olympic kebab.
Look left, black painted hoarding of a site of intermittent use,
A lonely greyhound nods. New granite setts awake.

Onwards to the junction!
Low, a guerrilla garden and some requisitioned estate agent
sticks.
A bit further; a pearl can be found for those needing to connect.

Wallis continues to the right,
'Plastic was invented here.'
Then a mechanic's, a book distributor and a printer,
To nearly end at an industrial estate;
Artists work here.

Behind the metal mesh and blue steel gateway,
Looking further, the River Lea.
Sometimes rowing boats, sometimes barges.
Often orange security, mostly weekend strollers.


The towpath – the Capital Ring – an orbit of motion to Old Ford
Lock.
Afar the legacy, a possible bridge.

A media centre and a landscape of intent.

# Paper Corpse

*By Rosie Higham-Stainton*

I stabbed the red button and a "ping" echoed through the carriage. The bus rolled to a stop and I stepped down onto the pavement. It loomed in front of me, the derelict fortress, crammed full of empty space. I stared up at the mass of discoloured concrete and yellowing brick, and above it, the sky in thick swathes of cartoon blue, so bright that little jabbing pains tormented my eyes.

It wasn't always like this. I mean, the bus stop didn't change, nor did the itchy collar of my uniform, or the sticky handle of the plastic carrier bag I was holding. But each day was a different backdrop – sometimes it would be streaks of rain and heavy clouds, or the white smog that our city is famous for. People swarm past me on the pavement, pushing onwards down Hackney Road, headed for the City, determined that this morning they would be on time; this morning they would not have to endure the tutting look of their seniors, way up high in the glass turrets of Bishopsgate or Bank.

Sucking in air, I headed towards the side entrance, eyelids already feeling heavier, my bag – yesterday's Evening Standard, corn beef sandwiches, a packet of Quavers – a dead weight in my hand. I rounded the corner to the side of the building that sits in darkness, towering so high that the sun's rays were eclipsed. The muddle of pokey windows and rusty fire escapes wallowed in their Victorian gloom. A set of stairs led down to the cellar door – our entrance – and as I took them darkness encroached, one step at a time. I felt the mechanics of the lock grind, click open and with me flooded in a rare streak of natural light, dimming the fluorescent glow of the television screens that lined one wall. But as the heavy bulk of the door snapped shut, it was gone again. I was left with Pat, strewn out on a plastic chair in front of me underneath the bulb lighting, his limbs hanging down, eyes shut, mouth open. I dumped my bag on the desk, strewn with polystyrene teacups and day-old newspapers. I stood over him, his awkwardly angled body the same as it was every morning, splayed out, sparkers. I nudged his shin with the tip of my boot and he sprung to life, hoiking himself back onto the seat of the chair and blinking.

'Arh, a'right Jim,' he said groggily, looking up at me, 'how you been?'

As if I was an old pal he hadn't seen in months.

He rubbed his eyes. I clenched my jaw. It was the same line every time, and every time I wanted to shrink further into my shirt, which was already two sizes too big. In answer, in my head, I recalled the nothingness of the previous night, the smell of Lambert and Butler turning to ash in the yellow dish, the grainy TV in need of a new aerial.

My routine answer was, 'Yeah not bad, Pat. Any trouble last night?' But the words didn't come out. Any trouble? Considering the man was unconscious each morning, how would he know? He rose to his feet. I realised I had been standing over him, a little too close for a little too long.

'Right, best be home to the missus. Bye lad,' he called over his shoulder as he reached the door.

He yanked it open. Once more, a flash of light filled the room. Once more the weighty mass of the door forced it out, this time, with an echoing slam. I sunk down into one of the plastic chairs, soaked in darkness except for the CCTV screens flickering irregularly. It was beginning again. A day of night. My ungodly routine, to guard this discarded place, to listen to the rats scuttle, the faint electrical buzz from the equipment. No radio though, for lack of signal. No light so as to go unnoticed. This was my life. I leant back in the chair and felt the numbing sensation spread across me. It was my body's form of protection against the silence, armour against the insanity it could conjure.

*** 

Who am I? I am the thing in the cellar. I am the rustling sound he mistakes for vermin and pigeons. I am the one who was left behind. My sisters and friends, Betty our ward nurse, all taken. Typhoid and pneumonia mostly. I wasn't so lucky. I was left alone, to reign over this vacant labyrinth of broken floorboards and rotting walls. The smell of decay is choking; I have never become accustomed to it. Far worse than the fumes that would drift from the operation theatre where old Mr Walter would poke around in the "Cancerous ones". I didn't befriend them. What was the point? We all knew they would be gone before Christmas. But the smell, yes the smell. At least flesh rots and recedes, vanishing eventually, but the bones of this place decompose so slowly, acid rain eating away at everything. The stench of wood and wallpaper fermenting, of putrid fungus, has plagued this place for so long that I wonder whether it will ever come down.

This morning, I peered through the grime-coated window, from the ground floor visiting room as the bus halted outside. Everything was muted by the layer of dirt and cobwebs that separated me from that world. I watched the blurred, dark form disembark and round the corner of the building. I crawled across the room, dodging strewn rubble and upturned boards, to the hole in the floor in the corner. Dropping to my knees, then down again until I lay in a bed of dust, I peered through the cavity where some ventilation pipe had been, catching a glimpse of the two men's heads. They were both standing now. The young one, with his hands in his pockets. I wasn't interested in the old man; he snored all night, his body limp and flabby. To me, the boy was Arthur incarnate, my beloved older brother who had never returned from war. He was Arthur, this was our game of hide and seek. Their conversation was just a murmur against the rumble of the buses outside and soon the door slammed leaving Arthur alone in the centre of the room, half of him illuminated by the glowing boxes on the wall.

He sat down and was very still for a long time. How long? I don't know. There seems little point in counting. Time is irrelevant. I rested my chin on the back of my hands and watched him, wondering, as I did most days, what he thought about during these hours of silence. I would shut my eyes and pretend I was one of the doctors who used to come and "observe", they called it, during visiting hours. With their fingertips together, forming a triangle, they would sit and watch us. They knew something that we didn't. I still don't know what that something was. My chest heaved a long and silent sigh at the comfort Arthur unknowingly brought me; maybe he had made it back after all. Every morning as the boy stepped off the bus, I had the same sensation that he was home and everything would be as it should.

After some time I pulled myself up, wiping away the years of dust that clung to my trousers. Tiptoeing across the room and out into the hall, I descended the stairs and wound through corridors to my favourite observation spot. It was a broom cupboard that backed onto their bunker. Part of the wall, low down, had rotted leaving a perfectly formed viewing hole. From there I could sense human warmth. Even a hand flinching was a comfort of sorts.

At the beginning I had been careful, breathing as quietly as my airwaves would allow. For years I wondered how he couldn't sense my presence. Then one day, I realised, feeling the stone cold skin of my own arm, that the inactive cells of my body gave off no heat, no hum. It made me sloppy in my bid to go unnoticed.

Once, not long ago, I had crouched, in exactly the same spot, peering through at him, both of us lost in his thoughts. Without realising, I knocked a discarded plank with my foot. The noise reverberated around the tiny cupboard. I froze, pressing my lips firmly shut. I watched his head jerk to the side. He slowly peered round in the direction of the wall behind which I cowered. I ducked my head and there was silence but I could feel him still staring in my direction. He had thought it a rat. I kept still for a long time, not wanting to chance it. I moved backwards out through the cupboard door, catching my foot on another plank of wood that rolled over with a little thud. The feet of the chair screeched this time, and I bolted up the stairs wishing my body to be lighter.

'You bloody things!' I heard him yell.

He must have been standing in the doorway because his voice echoed up the stair well. I had gone. Up I went, and up further, climbing the next set of stairs on tiptoes, so as not to be heard. Above my head was a scrap of sky where the roof had partly collapsed. A broad smile had spread across my face. I laughed silently gulping in air as I neared the top. Then the opening was directly above me and I collapsed to the floor. The disgruntled pigeons ruffled their feathers and flew out into sky, circling and squawking. I lay staring up at them, dozens of black dots against the overcast sky. My mind tingled. I only wished my body would do the same.

I had grown wiser since then, learning where each loose floorboard lay. Yet, it was impossible to predict the constant decay of this prison. So this morning, I crouched in my favourite spot. Some hours must have passed since his exchange with the old guard and his reassuring presence had sent me into semi-sleep. Just as my head bobbed forward, a large drop of water hit my neck and trickled down inside my shirt collar. I cried out with surprise and there was the rustling of newspaper on the other side of the wall. I tried to get onto my feet but stumbled. He had already appeared at the cupboard entrance. I felt his dark shadow blocking out any light there was.

'What the?!' he yelled.

I was still on the floor cowering, with my arms protecting my face. I shifted my arm and saw him towering over me, a leaf of crumpled newspaper still in his hand. His mouth hung open and he blinked.

'What are you doing in here?' he shouted, louder than necessary.

'I—'

'You cant be in here. It's too dangerous. There's asbestos everywhere, you—' he trailed off. I felt him staring at me but didn't dare look up. I tried to guess the succession of thoughts in his brain. The newspaper was quivering in his hand.

'I've heard you before haven't I. Creeping about with the rats.' He was shaking his head. I had let my arms drop but was still pinned to the wall in horror.

'Get up and get out of here.' He said motioning me up. I staggered to my feet.

'I can't. I mean I can't get out of here.'

'What do you mean you can't? This is no place for kids.'

'But it is. It's—' I hesitated. He was closer now; I didn't know who was more afraid.

'Look, you are going to have to get out,' he repeated.

'But I can't. I told you. I can't get out. This is where I live. It's where I've always been.'

'What do you mean? You're a squatter?'

His voice was gruffer than Arthur's, tinted with an accent that I didn't recognise. I looked at him blankly and watched his expression alter. He knew. He knew that I wasn't really there, that I was no courageous schoolboy goaded into this place by a pack of giggling children. We were silent for a long time.

'Get in there,' he said suddenly. I stumbled through to the guard's bunker, his hand gripping the shoulder of my sweater. I sat down on the floor, my arms wrapped around my knees. He moved the chair so that he sat facing me. In the relative light of the room, we became clearer to one another. At first I kept my eyes on the floor, counting the particles of rock that covered these cellar rooms. I felt him studying my face, its pale skin and hollow cheeks. I imagined that my eyeballs stood out too much, stretching the skin around them, but in reality I had no idea. I hadn't seen a mirror in a long time. When I did look up, his face was taught, eyes wide with fear, with confusion, with the prospect of insanity.

'Shit,' he whispered under his breath. 'What are you doing in here?' He spoke softly now, the initial shock subsiding.

'Well, this is where I live, I told you,' I replied, plucking up some courage.

He was shaking his head, but I pushed on, asking, 'Why are you here?'

He snorted. I wasn't sure what was funny.

'Good question.'

Then there was silence again. I looked up. It was him, I was sure of it. The broken nose from playing rugby, his thick straw-like hair. Only now it was greased back with wax.

'You are Arthur aren't you?' I said it without thinking. Without meaning to.

'Aye? No, who's Arthur?'

He seemed suspicious now.

My shoulders sunk down and my limbs felt heavy with tiredness.

'Who's Arthur?'

I looked at the floor.

'I'm speaking to you, who's Arthur?' He was trying to sound stern, like the matron used to, but he faltered too much.

'My brother. You look a lot like him,' I replied.

He leaned forward, his elbows resting on his knees. He massaged his eyelids with the tips of his fingers.

'This place is sending me mental,' he muttered.

Everything he said was under his breath, as if I wasn't there at all. I felt lethargic and my limbs were numbing. I wanted to explain to him, to reassure him. I didn't have the words. I didn't know what I was. I had been a little boy, in a hospital bed, trying to get better. What part of him was still left? I didn't feel the drafts that whistled through the cracks, nor the pangs of hunger that invariably come after decades without food. The only thing I ever felt was tiredness, tiredness so strong that my limbs may as well have been stone. It wasn't Arthur. I could see that now. But, maybe he was another version, the living version and in that there was something soothing.

It was creeping up on me, the tiredness. I shuffled down until I was lying on my side in the centre of the room, legs pulled up to my stomach.

'Can I... I'm so tired. Can I just rest a minute Arthur?'

I couldn't control it. Lethargy took over.

***

There he lay, curled up in a ball in the centre of the room. This pale creature I didn't dare touch in case he was how he seemed, cold and lifeless. I tried to imagine that he lived off rats and pigeons, collecting rainwater from the pipes on the roof. This hypothesis dissolved before it had time to fully form. Who was I kidding? He wasn't a street child. He was a prisoner in this place, living off air and his memories that filled the corridors. The shrieks of laughter and painful howls. I sat for hours, watching him sleep silently. There were no muffled exhalations of breath. Neither did he flinch or shuffle. He lay deadly still on the concrete. I considered telling Pat, but what would I say and what would we do with something like this, neither human nor dead. I was pretty sure social services didn't have a place for them. Maybe I could take him home to Ma but a dementia-ridden woman of sixty was no parent for this child, or any. I looked at my watch. Ten minutes until changeover.

Rising up, I walked over to where he lay, my back stiff from sitting for too long. I crouched down, wriggled my arms under his body. His skin was waxy and cold. I heaved him up, expecting to struggle but lost balance as I rose. He weighed no more than a packet of bread rolls. Remembering that there were only a few minutes spare before Pat's arrival I carried the boy out into the passageway. He started to stir in my arms, rubbing his eyes and his body became heavier. I would not make the stairs if he woke fully, so instead I carried him over to the broom cupboard. I laid him down on the floor. He shuffled, but didn't fully open his eyes. There was the sound of a key in the lock and I darted out and back into the bunker, slouching into the chair as Pat threw the door open.

That night, as Ma complained about the dodgy TV aerial and narrated the story of her afternoon spent in the post office with Fred Astaire, I wondered whether he had woken. Whether Pat had found him curled up, just the other side of that wall. The next morning, I was relieved to find Pat splayed out as usual. When I woke him we muttered our well-rehearsed exchange and then he left, clunking the door firmly shut. I stood in the darkness, searching the space for sounds, a shuffle of foot or a voice. Nothing. I hurried down the corridor to the cupboard. It was empty, except for a couple of wooden planks. Back in the room, I slumped down into the plastic chair. It was still warm from Pat's hefty weight. In the corner of my eye, I noticed something irregular on one of monitors. I leapt to my feet, but as I neared the row of screens I realised it was just skipping and stuttering. A faulty signal. I moved along the row, peering at each shot, right up close, searching the murky grey for a small dark thing, an irregularity. Nothing materialised.

Maybe this was it, I thought as I stood with my eyes fixed on the end screen. I was going the same way as Ma. What made seeing bloodless children more rational than believing you had danced around the post office with a Hollywood actor dead and buried? Early onset dementia they called it, or perhaps it was some other form of madness. At any rate, here in the darkness, who was there to define insanity? My eyes started to ache. 'They'll turn square if you sit too near the screen,' Ma used to say. I moved away, rubbing them gently. I picked up the day's paper as an optimistic distraction, but every creak and draft jolted me back into that cell of a room, the desolate corridors that encircled it and the vacant spaces way above. Finally, I fell into the plot of a murder up on the Pembury estate. The photo on page twelve was a muddle of police officers in a car park. White tape everywhere, but no real activity.

I heard something roll part way across the room. Near my feet lay a small piece of rubble. He was there, somewhere close by, hiding. I thought of calling out to him. Instead I stood up as silently as my nylon trousers would allow, strode across to the door, peered out into the hall. He was curled up in a ball, an identical pose to the day I found him in the broom cupboard. This time he didn't cover. He had wanted to be found, to be let into this cage. He knew where I was, he knew how to watch me and go unseen. I was the caged animal. I was an amusing pet for this boy, if he was even that. What name is there for something that is as light as a crumpled paper bag when it sleeps?

I jerked my head, signalling him to get up. He scrambled to his feet, and slowly followed me into the room. I sat back down on the chair. Taking a new tack, I flipped open the paper again and pretended to read. He was still standing, in the middle of the room just like before and was the first to speak.

'Why are you here? This isn't your home. Where do you go at night?'

I stared at the piece of rubble on the floor, mulling over an answer.

'It's my Ma,' I said, wanting to divert from the subject already yet not knowing how. 'I'm here because of my Ma,' I repeated, with more conviction this time. I wasn't sure which one of us I was trying to sell that line to.

'What, your mother keeps you in here? What did you do?'

The boy was staring at me now, an expression of horror hanging around his open mouth. A small snort escaped my mouth.

'Something like that,' I mumbled.

'Well, what did you do? You must have done something bad.'

He was studying my face. I saw his dull grey eyes become sharp and my palms grew sticky.

'No, that's not what I mean. Of course she doesn't keep me in here. I'm working aren't I?'

'Oh.' He paused. 'But you said that she —'

'No I'm in here to work. Work for money, you know?' I said, now raising my eyebrows as I looked at him for a sign of comprehension.

'Oh, I see.' He paused again, as if proofreading everything he said and thought.

I started up, 'We have to have money to eat and…she's sick, so she needs medicine. It's expensive, that stuff.'

'But why here? Do you like this place too?'

My eyes began to sting, as I looked down at this spindly figure and the sincerity in his eyes.

It came out, uncontrollably. 'Because it's a job, okay!' I said, louder now.

'And do I like it? No. Every day, when that door shuts I think I lose another fragment of my mind. It's a prison, you do realise that, don't you? And we both are completely fucking trapped. This place is going to kill me, and apparently it has already killed you.'

I stopped. I had just told a child he was dead. I didn't even know what he was or if he was. Now it was he who stared at the chip of rubble. He wouldn't lift his eyes.

Still staring, he said softly, 'You're not dead yet though.'

He began to slide down onto the floor, until he was curled up again with his eyes heavily shut.

Again, he slept, without a snuffle or snore. I sat watching him. I thought of the ashtray full of stained stubs at home. The smell of the bleach that Ma used to relentlessly scrub the bath that nobody used. I thought of the mass of darkness outside my bedroom window, save for the twinkling glow of the TV screens in the flats opposite ours. I tried to picture it all in the midday light. I couldn't. I didn't know what that looked like anymore. My hands covered my face. I felt the sticky film from them transfer onto my cheeks. Tears followed, small but explosive gurgles that reverberated in my cupped hands.

He slept on, deaf to the sound of human emotion, handcuffed to the emptiness of this place.

I don't know how long I sat watching the sleeping boy. I was stirred by the thud of rubber soles on pavement outside, and the murmur and giggles. It was gone three o'clock, probably nearing four. The school children would be rambling homeward in packs. I stood up, breathing heavily, feeling like my chest would explode if I didn't get real air, see daylight.

But the boy. I couldn't just abandon him. I stood over him again, stared at his fragile and brittle mass. This time, as I lifted him, he didn't stir. He hung from my arms, long limbed, nearly weightless. After I had placed him in the cupboard I returned to the room, folded up the paper. All that was left to do was wait for the day to finish. I sat for the last time, listening to the scutter and creaks, breathing in the emptiness that had enveloped me for so long. It was broken by the click of the top Yale lock. Pat stood in the doorway, silhouetted by the last of the evening light and an indigo sky. I jumped up and pushed past him without saying anything.

'Hey lad, watch it,' he said as he stumbled from the doorway.

'Well I'll see you tomorrow?' he called after me, a sour tone to his voice, a rib at my rudeness.

'I guess you haven't heard then?' he continued, but I was gone.

I craned my neck up at the sky as I walked away, sucking in cold air. When I reached the corner of Hackney Road I stopped, listened to the lorry engines and cackles from the last of the school children who had stayed out late, feasting on boxes of fried chicken. I breathed in the smell of the cooking oil and the exhaust pipe fumes. A stream of keep-fit office workers swam up Hackney Road heading home. I started off in the same direction. My strides got longer, faster, until I was running, sprinting along the pavement, not seeming to lose a breath. I ran on, not looking back. Not daring to in case the windows swallowed me back in. I turned off and eventually came to a stop, slumping down on a park bench. I sat panting, in the grainy last shades of light. It had been done. That was it. There wouldn't be another morning like today's. I wouldn't have to see the light shut out. I thought of him, curled up in the broom cupboard. Alive, dead, real? I didn't know. He was there still, that much I did know, trapped within those peeling walls. I unbuttoned the top of my shirt, feeling the sweat that had collected at the nape of my neck.

By the time I left the electrical shop, its windows cluttered with dusty PC monitors and stereo systems, the city was in darkness. I thought of her crinkled old face as I came in the door with the newly purchased aerial, the lines around her mouth morphing into a smile. Unlocking the front door and shoving it with my knee, the smell of bleach hit me, artificial lemon. Then a breeze carried away the smell, a breeze I didn't recognise in this usually stagnant space. I heard the TV blaring at the other end of the hallway, and could see the curtain in the lounge billowing against the open window. I walked towards it, slowly at first, then faster sensing that Ma wasn't in there. Coming into the room my eyes made for the armchair. It was empty. So was the settee, except for each cushion in its rightful place. I began to shake. I set the aerial down on the table. I stood, waiting as I had done in the cellar, waiting to hear a rustle from the bedroom, or her calling my name from the toilet. Nothing. I edged towards the open window, pulled back the curtain which fought my taming hands and tried to yank free. I looked out into the dark, down at the car park. She lay there, on the cold concrete a frail doll-like creature, accentuated more by the distance between us. I let out a whimper. It echoed between the tower blocks.

A week later they tore it down. I was passing on the bus with no intention of getting off at that stop. As we drew up I saw the wooden fencing built up around it and the claws of diggers snatching at its skeleton. I realised, then, that this was what Pat had been trying to tell me. Trying to explain that I could leave, because there was no job for me anymore. I had been set free. Before the doors beeped shut, I scrambled up and off the bus. Men in hard hats were wheel-barrowing out debris. I ran through their entrance and up the main steps. A man yelled after me but I was already through the foyer and climbing the stairs. I had to get him out, before it came down. I didn't want the fragile boy to be pummelled against the concrete like Ma had been. There had to be more than one survivor. I sucked in air to shout his name, before remembering I did not know it, had never known it. I climbed further, hearing floorboards crack under my heel.

'BOYYYY!' I screamed. The sound filled the stairwell, but only the pigeons replied with their coos, flapping up in the rafters.

I had slowed down, panting again and feeling things give way under my feet.

'Oi, you cant be in 'ere mate. It's not safe,' one of the hard-hatted men called from the bottom.

I clung onto the rotting banister. Soon he had caught up with me, laying a firm hand on my back.

'Come on mate. You don't want to die in 'ere.'

He led me down the stairs and out into daylight. My eyes stung from the light and I crouched on the floor shading them. I had been right. We had both been prisoners not just of that place, but of lifeless corpses too, wandering in an empty labyrinth. Only I had been allowed out. I heard the thuds of bricks and mortar as the decaying mass tumbled down. Plumes of chalky dust rose up in its place. I waited for a feeble yelp or echo from inside.

Nothing.

# Wicklove

*By Siddhartha Bose*


Two years ago I met this cinnamon girl with glasses and a mean-child tribal-smile at the Wicked festival.

(Her hair fit for the shape of
       brown deserts. When it
           falls it flecks
              the laughter of her gods. Her
nose is a cat, leopard lips. Her
       neck the perfection of a lemon whose green
        bleeds my eyes)


Chicken-shopped, corner-kebabed, glimmer dereliction, Hackney Wick — chromatic — fizzes, bobs, pops in soap bubbles, like tube-travellers on a plunkt escalator.
(How do you make this
      city a spirit, she asks, when
          all you see is a plant without roots?

       She is more than here. My fear is incense.)

***

Outside the festa hums — carnival eyes ears hands hips lips edge 'n' slither round the wasteland of white caravans blaring Nirvana, bulldog-chained, locked. Clouds curve 'n' streak like elegant-ringed fingers. Paintbrush pink. Blotched impressions. Carnival raves glow in dungeons under the rush 'n' cum of the highway by Victoria park sanitation.

On Felstead street the old Bedlam performers fizzle — old man lookin' like an Amish prophet, long-haired and black-hatted, limp-walking, silent 'n' slow, stinkpissing. Next to him there's Clara with her whistle-gun laugh, her fractured teeth 'n' glasses. Hovering bird-like over them there's Bigfoot, waddling like a duck, blind 'n' bearded, headed for his four-cheeseburger fix.

(I wonder what they make of this performed bohemia?)

***

Round them, Hackney erupts. Art imaginings. Studios are prehistoric caves, Fela-music laces the canal, punkstep grinds hard in the Lord Napier, hoodies hunt 'n' sell tornado ketamine, and graffiti—dinosaur bloodstains, magic map-ruins—lead our way.

(Inside we sit surrounded by plants.

A cat curled, framed window, salmon sky.

A crane sticks out like a fishbone.


She tells me stories about her ancestral village in Greece, of a lake called Clara with reincarnated fish. When I say all art is shamanic, she nods, sticking her tongue in my rib-hole.

Interstellar contortions, mystical fibula.


When I ask about Olympus—

rivering down a blank alleyway by Fish

Island—she, hair electric, smiles in salt rain.)


***

The first night, in the abandoned car-park with litter graffiti off White Post Lane — cockroach eyes, space warriors, dragon souls — we pop. She reaches out, ruffles my razor-head, cleaning my aura.

('It's heavy,' she says
in a wink)

She don't like reggae. I cringe.

(Wandering, I
see the lines on my
face in a glowing crystal ball in a Spanish squat in
St. Mary's church.

I am more than one person, one place).

\*\*\*

At home, we dance to MJ, greet the morning twirling to silk jazz.
(that killa rendition of *Autumn Leaves* on
*Somethin' else.* The
smoke-oil musk in my skin kills her.
We sleep alone.)

\*\*\*

Next day I take the stage with beatboxers, throbbing my rhymes. A devil-dread worshipper, shamanic, muscles through the crowd, sinks in mud, trance-hipped and wild, gives me the finger.

Nighttime, the wickerman burns, fireflies abound — tribal sound emancipation.

We stray, salting our way to the Peanut Factory. Find ourselves in a net with bouncing balls. We throw them at each other, laughing, pealing like onions.

By the canal, we levitate. Fairy monsters. Scum-cop helicopters float 'n' cut currents above us. We shoo them away like bloodsucking mosquitoes, become one in defiance.

Below there's Hackney in pink — river-shroud, rave-rotted incantation. Prayers join us in love.
 (Morning spills like milk.
                         The sky is molten lead,
                                            like a surgeried heart.
                                                        My child is me.)

# Acknowledgments

The editors would like to thank all of the contributors, Tom at Penned in the Margins for all the help and advice, Tom at Legend Press, Chris Smisson for solving our complete lack of design skills, Lee, Gavin and Tim for their invaluable guidance, Kashmir Kebabish for all the cheap curry, Bootstraps for the office space, Café Oto for the caffeine, Joe and Jim from the Independent Content Company, Rebekah Robertson for the superhuman proof reading, Frank and Geri for the Gosling-esque driving skills, Stewart Home, Owen Jones, Laura Oldfield Ford, Dee, Meghna, Sarah, Centerprise, Pages of Hackney, Biddles, Edd and the London Zine Symposium, Jimi at Alternative Press, and everyone else who took an interest in the project or helped us in any way.

# Biographical Notes

**Sam Berkson** (Angry Sam) has been performing poetry since 2002 when his first ever public poetry performance ended in a fight. Since then he has promoted live shows for the poetry collective, Hammer and Tongue, performed at gigs across the country and at festivals in the UK and abroad.

In the process, he was for a while the Brighton Festival Slam Champion and the Liverpool Capital of Culture Slam Champion. A poetry promoter once said about him, '*Angry Sam kills the crowd softly with rare wit and a laid back style that softens the knife wounds left by his acid political poetics and searing urban imagery*' - Martin Daws, POETica. He lives near Hackney Downs.

**Siddartha Bose** is a writer, performer, and filmmaker based in Hackney, London. He grew up in India, followed by a seven-year stint in the USA. His poetry has appeared in *City State: New London Poetry* (Penned in the Margins, 2009), *Voice Recognition; 21 Poets for the 21st Century* (Bloodaxe, 2009) and *The HarperCollins Book of Modern English Poetry by Indians* (HarperCollins, 2011).

His first book of poetry, *Kalagora*, appeared last year (Penned in the Margins, 2010). He has also written, performed, and toured a one-man theatre show, also *Kalagora*, which is headed for the Edinburgh Fringe later this year. He is currently developing a full-length play with WhynotTheatre, Toronto, and was dubbed one of the *'ten rising stars of British poetry'* by *The Times* (UK)

**Gavin James Bower** was born and raised in Lancashire and now lives in London. He is the author of two novels, and his writing has appeared in *3:AM Magazine, Pen Pusher, The White Review, Clash, Culture Wars, FLUX* and the *Sunday Telegraph*.

**Isaura Barbé-Brown** is an actress and writer born and raised in Hackney. She left London to study acting at The American Academy of Dramatic Arts in New York for three years. She moved back in 2008 and has done some work in fringe theatre as well as starring in the short film *Mosa* which was part of the Gay and Lesbian film Festival at the BFI. She also just finished playing the lead in the feature film *David is Dying* which will soon be screened around London.

She writes a film blog *If they film it, I will come* and is currently writing her first novel.

She tutors teenagers and adults in English Literature and Drama.

**Gary Budden** is the co-editor of the anthology *Acquired for Development By...* He has worked for *Ambit* magazine, Stoke Newington Literary Festival, Richmond Literature Festival and the British Film Institute, amongst other things. He loves punk rock, literature, and being a vegetarian.

**Tim Burrows** writes for *The Daily Telegraph*, *New Statesman*, *Dazed & Confused*, *The Quietus*, *The Stool Pigeon* and *Tank*. His book on music venues, *From CBGB to the Roundhouse*, was published in 2009. He contributes to Resonance FM's *Hello Goodbye Show* in the form of essays and interviews, and plays drums in Private Trousers.

**Kit Caless** is the co-editor of the anthology *Acquired for Development By...* He is the founder and editor of *Stalking Elk*. He is the presenter of the *Sunday Matinee Show* and spoken word show *Re:Versed* on NTS Radio. He was runner up on cheating Channel 5 quiz show, *Brainteaser* in 2005. Kit loves hip hop (cos he never dug disco), "transgressional" fiction and whiskey.

**Paul Case** (Captain of the Rant) resides in Stoke Newington and has been performing poetry and spoken word since May 2008. He has shared stages with some of the biggest names in poetry, and played festivals such as Secret Garden Party and Glastonwick, and has appeared twice to perform on radical radio programme *Dissident Island*.

His poetry has been published in a diverse array of publications, from *The Erotic Review* to *Class War*. He has co-organised poetry and music events, festivals, all dayers and curated his own weekly, month-long residency called the Basement Sedition. He fully intends to spend the rest of his life in much the same manner, and is consistently amazed that his big mouth has never once got him beaten up.

**Ashlee Christoffersen** works in the lesbian, gay, bisexual and trans (LGBT) community sector and previously worked in the trade union movement and in academia as a researcher. She has a Masters Degree in gender studies and her writing on gender, equality, and/or Marxism has appeared in diverse and random publications, including the punk mag *Last Hours*, feminist DIY zines and the academic journal *British Politics*. She's recently authored a book on LGBT organising in London, *The London LGBT Voluntary and Community Sector Almanac*.

**David Dawkins** is the manager of Pages of Hackney bookshop and a graduate of the Creative Writing MA at Goldsmiths College. His journalism has appeared in a variety of publications from *Dazed & Confused* to *The Hackney Citizen* and he is currently writing his first novel, *Euth*.

**Anita DeMahy** is a native of Seattle who moved to London a few years ago. She is currently working on a collection of short stories while completing her MA in Creative Writing at London Metropolitan University.

**Kieran Duddy** is originally from Derry, in Northern Ireland. He has been living in London for twenty years. He is currently working on a novel and a selection of short stories that are set in Northern Ireland. His favourite pastimes are drinking coffee, smoking cigarettes and listening to punk rock.

**Laura Oldfield Ford** has become well known for her politically active and poetic engagement with London as a site of social antagonism. She both imagines a future London whilst simultaneously sifting through the detritus of history, depicting dystopian scenes, class conflict and urban ruins using ballpoint pen, fluorescent spray paint and acrylic. She exhibits and teaches across Europe and America. Her new book, *Savage Messiah*, collects together the entire set of her fanzine to date. Part graphic novel, part artwork, the book is both an angry polemic against the marginalization of the city's working class and an exploration of the cracks that open up in urban space.

**Nell Frizzell** is a freelance writer, editor and nimble-fingered seamstress living on the banks of the River Lea in Clapton. Nell studied English at Leeds University, where she also worked for two years as magazine editor at *The Leeds Guide*. However, in the end, the pull to The Big Smoke became too strong. Since moving to London she has worked as a copywriter, a marketing officer, a semi-professional knitter and assistant editor.

**Natalie Hardwick** is a semi-freelance journalist working for the BBC and contributing to *The Guardian*, *The Stool Pigeon* and *Clash* magazines. Her interests lie primarily in food and music, mainly of the Northern variety on both counts, but as an honorary Claptonite also enjoys writing and mingling for community titles like *Hackney Citizen*. She recently ventured into beer writing, ergo she is most at ease when manning an ale pump

**Rosie Higham-Stainton** is a writer living and working in Hackney. She has contributed to creative online publications including *Somethinkblue* and *Ribbed Magazine*, run by emerging young writers and artists.

Rosie completed her BA at Goldsmiths College in 2009, where she took full advantage of the creative writing facilities, and since then has been involved with events at Writers' Centre Norwich and English PEN. Through the independent bookshop she manages, Rosie has been able to establish a yearly programme of literary events, working with local schools and authors to make books and literature accessible to everyone.

**Daniel Kramb** is the author of the Hackney-set debut novel *Dark Times* and the self-published haiku collection *Three Lines Towards*. Popshot Magazine has published *F-Word*, a poem about our general abuse of the word freedom. *Open Wide Magazine* featured the recession-themed short story *Departure*.

Daniel has lived in Hackney since 2004 (excluding the year 2010, which he spent in Amsterdam).

**Georgia Myers** grew up in Hackney and has lived there for most of her life; she has tried to escape a few times, but can't quite bring herself to leave. She went to Kingsland Secondary School, did Art History at Sussex University, and then worked at the BBC. She has been writing for the past eight years and lives with her husband and three children.


**Molly Naylor** is a writer and performer. Her poems have been featured on BBC Radio 4 and in publications including *The Rialto*. She has performed at events and festivals all over the world including Latitude, Glastonbury, Palabra y Musica, The Big Chill, Poet in the City, Edinburgh Festival Fringe, Purple Ronnie's Stand Up Poetry Club, Shunt, Soho Theatre and many more. She has a Masters in Creative Writing from the University of East Anglia. Her solo spoken word show – *Whenever I Get Blown Up I Think Of You* is produced by Sarah Ellis and Apples & Snakes.

An illustrated book of her show is available from Nasty Litte Press. She is currently working on a sitcom and a new live show.

*'A rising light of the London poetry scene'* – *The Independent*


**Eithne Nightingale** works as Head of Diversity at the V&A Museum and is editing a book on museums, equality and social justice to be published by Routledge in 2012. Over the last four years she has had travel, fiction and memoir writing published both in the UK and in Australia. She won two categories of the Arts Council sponsored Writers, inc Writers of the Year Award in 2008.

She lives in Hackney, where she has lived for over thirty years and worked for fourteen years at Hackney Community College before going to the V&A.

**Ania Ostrowska** moved to London from post-communist Poland to pursue an academic career, enabled by her country's joining the EU. To sanction her feminist credentials, she got an MA in Gender Studies from SOAS.

She has lived in Hackney for a year-and-a-half and is very happy about cycling around the borough and very unhappy about marching gentrification of the area. She divides her time between working part-time at the Wellcome Library and reaching a conclusive position on the UK feminist movement.

**Brendan Pickett** is an experimenter with words, sound and visual forms. He studied at St Martin's Art College, worked in a photography studio developing paparazzi pictures and has produced music for numerous bands he has played in. As well as composing music for gay porn he currently plays bass in the Hackney based funk-bashment-reggae band The Common. He writes and performs experimental poetry, short stories and satirical routines.

**Colin Priest** is a local designer operating between the fields of art, architecture, urbanism and events at a variety of scales with an ambition to create memorable contemporary experiences. Trained as an architect, his inter-disciplinary collaborative practice centres on adjusting the cultural value of contemporary public space, shifting perceptions of identity, society and notions of locality. Having lived in Hackney since 2004 he has been based in Hackney Wick since 2008.

**Gareth Rees** is author of *The Marshman Chronicles*, a blog dedicated to Hackney & Walthamstow Marshes. He's written comedy for BBC radio and cringe worthy jingles for commercial radio. These days he's a freelance copywriter and one half of marketing duo The Free Radicals. He spends his remaining time obsessing over psychedelic music and is resident DJ in his own attic room.

He lives in Clapton with his wife and two daughters. He can be found wandering the marshes every afternoon with his trusty dog, Hendrix.


**Lee Rourke** is the author of the critically acclaimed debut novel *The Canal* (winner of *The Guardian*'s 'Not The Booker Prize' 2010) and the short story collection *Everyday*. A work of non-fiction *A Brief History of Fables: From Aesop to Flash Fiction* was released in September 2011. He lives in London.


### Andrea Watts

Andrea Watts is working on a collection of short stories; one has been published in the anthology *Dancing with Mr. Darcy* (Honno Press 2009); others have been short and long listed for BBC Radio Drama, the Fish Prize and the Bristol Competition. She is co-editing a short story anthology, *Echelon*, with fellow writers from Centerprise Trust, due out this year.

She lives in Hackney with her partner and their children.

INFLUX
PRESS

Influx Press is an independent publisher that specialises in
short run, responsive fiction.

We aim to publish challenging, controversial and alternative work that
is written in order to dissect and analyse our immediate surroundings
and produce site specific fiction and poetry.

Please visit

www.influxpress.com for extra material, including interviews

and videos with the authors.